FOUNDATIONS

of Restaurant Management & Culinary Arts

Level Two

Test Book with **EXAM**VIEW® Assessment Suite CD-ROM

National Restaurant Association

Prentice Hall

Boston Columbus Indianapolis New York San Francisco Upper Saddle River Amsterdam

Cape Town Dubai London Madrid Milan Munich Paris Montreal Toronto

Delhi Mexico City Sao Paulo Sydney Hong Kong Seoul Singapore Taipei Tokyo

Editorial Director: Vernon Anthony
Executive Editor: Wendy Craven
Editorial Assistant: Lenore Chait
Director of Marketing: David Gesell
Campaign Marketing Manager: Leigh Ann Sims
School Marketing Manager: Laura Cutone
Senior Marketing Assistant: Les Roberts
Associate Managing Editor: Alexandrina Benedicto Wolf
Project Manager: Kris Roach
Senior Operations Supervisor: Pat Tonneman
Operations Specialist: Deidra Skahill
Cover Designer: Jane Diane Ricciardi
Manager, Rights and Permissions: Zina Arabia

Cover Art: Kipling Swehla
NRAS Product Management Team: Janet Benoit, Megan Meyer, William Nolan, Rachel Peña, and Wendi Safstrom
Product Development and Project Management: Emergent Learning, LLC
Writing and Text Development: Kristine Westover, Michelle Graas, Michelle Somody, Tom Finn
Editorial and Composition: Claire Hunter and Abshier House
Printer/Binder: Courier Kendallville
Cover Printer: Phoenix Color

Prentice Hall
is an imprint of

PearsonSchool.com/careertech

ISBN 10:   0-13-138072-9
ISBN 13: 978-0-13-138072-1

Preface

This test book is designed to accompany *Foundations of Restaurant Management & Culinary Arts–Level Two*. The **EXAM**VIEW® CD-ROM that accompanies this test book includes all of the questions included in the print test book and allows you to generate customized exams and quizzes. The print component includes all the questions and answers from the test bank. The test bank includes questions in a variety of formats including true/false, multiple choice, short answer, and essay.

The **EXAM**VIEW® **Assessment Suite v.6.2** (including the **EXAM**VIEW® **Test Generator**, **EXAM**VIEW® **Test Manager**, and **EXAM**VIEW® **Test Player**) is a comprehensive solution for creating, administering, and scoring tests. The software includes many features to save you time and generate information to assess and improve student performance.

Teachers can use the **Test Generator** *to...*

- Create a paper test in less than five minutes.

- Print multiple versions of the same test.

- Enter your own questions.

- Prepare an online test, study guide, and worksheet.

Teachers can use the **Test Manager** *to...*

- Create or import a class roster.

- Automatically score a paper test using a scanner.

- Automatically score an assignment.

- Administer and score an online test.

- Prepare a variety of useful class and student reports.

Students can use the **Test Player** *to...*

- Take quizzes and tests using a local area network.

System Requirements

To use the **EXAM**VIEW® **Assessment Suite v.6.2**, your computer must meet or exceed the following minimum requirements:

Windows

- Microsoft Windows® 000/XP/Vista

- Intel Pentium® II 120 MHz or compatible processor

- 32 MB available memory for application (64 MB recommended)

- 32 MB of available hard drive space

- Monitor capable of displaying 16-bit color with 800 x 600 resolution

- Internet connection to access the content updater, software updater, and Web publishing features

Macintosh

- Mac OS X 10.2

- 120 MHz Power Macintosh (G3 recommended)

- 32 MB available memory for application (64 MB recommended)

- 28 MB of available hard drive space

- Monitor capable of displaying 16-bit color with 800 x 600 resolution

- Internet connection to access the content updater, software updater, and Web publishing features

Installation Instructions

Follow these steps to install the **EXAM**VIEW® **Assessment Suite.** The installer will automatically copy the question banks to a new folder within the **Banks** folder and may install an additional **Publish** folder for storing files that are needed for publishing questions to the publisher-hosted server.

1. Insert the disc into the CD-ROM drive of your computer.

   Windows: If the autorun feature is enabled on your computer, a window will automatically appear on your screen. Click the **Install** button and skip to step 5. If the autorun window does not appear, proceed to step 2.

   Macintosh: If necessary, open the installer window then double-click the **Exam-View Assessment Suite** installer icon. Proceed to step 5.

2. Click the **Start** button and choose **Run**.

3. In the Run window, type **d:\setup.exe**, replacing **d** with the drive letter that corresponds to the drive where the setup file is located.

4. Click the **OK** button.

5. Follow the instructions that appear on your screen.

6. Remove the installation disc when finished.

See the **Manual.pdf** file on the **EXAM**VIEW® CD-ROM for complete steps on getting started.

Table of Contents

Chapter 1
Breakfast Foods and Sandwiches

True/False

_____ 1. Cream contains far more fat than milk.

_____ 2. Margarine is a manufactured product that looks like butter but contains no milk products.

_____ 3. The main parts of a sandwich are the bread, filling, and spread.

_____ 4. Coffee should be brewed fresh and held for no longer than 2 hours.

_____ 5. Gorgonzola and romano are examples of grating cheeses.

Multiple Choice

1. Milk that has been heated to destroy harmful bacteria has been
   A. condensed.
   B. evaporated.
   C. pasteurized.
   D. homogenized.

2. Which type of butter has had its milk solids and water removed using heat?
   A. Ripened
   B. Clarified
   C. Whipped
   D. Pasteurized

3. What percentage of margarine's fat must come from fat?
   A. 20%
   B. 40%
   C. 60%
   D. 80%

4. The process in which dairies make cheese by separating a milk's solids from its liquid is called
   A. curdling.
   B. clarification.
   C. pasteurization.
   D. homogenization.

5. Cottage cheese and ricotta are examples of what type of cheese?
    A. Blue-veined
    B. Soft-ripened
    C. Firm, ripened
    D. Unripened, fresh

6. Which type of cheese has mold injected or sprayed into the cheese to spread throughout it while it ages?
    A. Blue-veined
    B. Soft-ripened
    C. Firm, ripened
    D. Unripened, fresh

7. What is the optimal temperature for storing cheese?
    A. 25°F to 35°F at a low humidity level
    B. 35°F to 45°F at a low humidity level
    C. 35°F to 45°F at a high humidity level
    D. 25°F to 35°F at a high humidity level

8. Refrigerated dairy products should be stored at or below which temperature?
    A. 21°F
    B. 31°F
    C. 41°F
    D. 51°F

9. Which part of an egg is also known as the albumen?
    A. Yolk
    B. Shell
    C. White
    D. Chalaza

10. Eggs cooked for immediate service should reach an internal temperature of _____ for 15 seconds.
    A. 135°F
    B. 145°F
    C. 155°F
    D. 165°F

11. Which form of egg is best for use in scrambled eggs or French toast?
    A. Fresh
    B. Dried
    C. Frozen
    D. Egg substitute

12. Eggs are constantly stirred during which cooking method?
    A. Frying
    B. Shirring
    C. Poaching
    D. Scrambling

13. Frying an egg on the bottom and then turning it over and frying it very lightly on its top side is called
    A. up.
    B. basted.
    C. over easy.
    D. scrambled.

14. A savory egg custard baked in a crust is called a(n)
    A. omelet.
    B. quiche.
    C. soufflé.
    D. frittata.

15. The cooking time for hard-boiled eggs is _____ minutes.
    A. 3
    B. 6
    C. 10
    D. 15

16. What size egg is the largest?
    A. Large
    B. Extra large
    C. Super large
    D. Jumbo

17. Soufflés are made with whipped
    A. egg yolks.
    B. egg whites.
    C. whole eggs.
    D. dried eggs.

18. Before cooking, French toast is dipped in a mixture of
    A. milk and eggs.
    B. flour and water.
    C. butter and eggs.
    D. egg yolks and sugar.

19. Bacon is about _____ percent fat.
    A. 35
    B. 45
    C. 60
    D. 70

20. Raw potatoes that have been peeled and then sliced, diced, or shredded are called
    A. home fries.
    B. brown hash.
    C. hash browns.
    D. French fries.

21. Brewing temperatures for coffee are between
    A. 175°F and 180°F.
    B. 185°F and 190°F.
    C. 195°F and 200°F.
    D. 205°F and 210°F.

22. Which type of tea has leaves that are fermented?
    A. White
    B. Black
    C. Green
    D. Yellow

23. A club sandwich is an example of a _____ sandwich.
    A. cold
    B. wrap
    C. submarine
    D. multidecker

24. A tuna melt is an example of a _____ sandwich.
    A. cold
    B. wrap
    C. grilled
    D. submarine

25. Which type of sandwich consists of two slices of bread or two halves of a roll, a spread, and a filling?
    A. Cold
    B. Wrap
    C. Submarine
    D. Multidecker

26. Butter and mayonnaise are common examples of
    A. spread.
    B. filling.
    C. garnish.
    D. condiment.

27. Lemon, chives, mustard, and honey are often used to flavor which sandwich ingredient?
    A. Bread
    B. Butter
    C. Ketchup
    D. Mayonnaise

28. On a hot dog with mustard, the mustard is the
    A. spread.
    B. filling.
    C. garnish.
    D. condiment.

29. On a turkey and cheese sandwich with mayonnaise, the turkey and cheese are the
    A. spread.
    B. filling.
    C. garnish.
    D. condiment.

30. Large, multidecker sandwiches or very thick sandwiches should be cut in
    A. half.
    B. thirds.
    C. quarters.
    D. eighths.

31. A canapé is sometimes served as a(n)
    A. condiment.
    B. hors d'oeuvre.
    C. club sandwich.
    D. grilled sandwich.

32. The best temperature range to store bread is
    A. 55°F to 65°F.
    B. 65°F to 75°F.
    C. 75°F to 85°F.
    D. 85°F to 95°F.

33. A Monte Cristo belongs to which category of sandwich?
    A. Cold
    B. Grilled
    C. Deep-fried
    D. Open-faced

34. Sandwiches prepared in advance should be stored
    A. covered in dry storage.
    B. uncovered in dry storage.
    C. covered in a refrigerator.
    D. uncovered in a refrigerator.

35. When steeping tea, make sure the tea leaves are exposed to water at a temperature of at least _____ for at least 5 minutes.
    A. 165°F
    B. 175°F
    C. 185°F
    D. 195°F

36. Which cooking method is used to make eggs benedict and eggs Florentine?
    A. Baking
    B. Frying
    C. Poaching
    D. Simmering

37. Cheddar and gruyère are examples of which type of cheese?
    A. Soft-ripened
    B. Firm, ripened
    C. Semisoft, ripened
    D. Very hard, ripened

38. In what part of the egg is fat found?
    A. Yolk
    B. White
    C. Shell
    D. Chalaza

39. A mixture of chopped meats, potatoes, and onions is called
A. grits.
B. hash.
C. home fries.
D. hash browns.

40. Shirred eggs are finished by
A. baking.
B. frying.
C. poaching.
D. simmering.

Short Answer

1. The point at which an oil or fat begins to burn is called the _____.

2. _____ eggs are fried and then steamed in a covered pan.

3. _____ tea is made from many different fruits and herbs and is naturally caffeine-free.

4. _____ is a hot, open-faced Italian pie with a crisp, yeast-dough bottom.

5. _____sandwiches are small, cold sandwiches usually served on bread or toast, trimmed of crusts, and cut into shapes.

Essay

1. Identify how to maintain an egg's quality and safety from receiving through preparation.

2. Compare and contrast bacon and Canadian bacon.

3. Is pizza a sandwich? Explain your answer.

Chapter 2
Nutrition

True/False

_____ 1. Vitamins do not provide any energy.

_____ 2. Simple carbohydrates are digested and absorbed quickly.

_____ 3. Complete proteins are called complete because they contain all essential fatty acids in the right amount.

_____ 4. The human body can live weeks without water.

_____ 5. The higher the temperature and the longer the cooking period, the less nutrient loss there will be.

Multiple Choice

1. The study of the nutrients in food and how they nourish the body is called
   A. nutrition.
   B. digestion.
   C. oxidation.
   D. absorption.

2. Dry beans, rice, and oatmeal are considered what type of carbohydrate?
   A. Simple
   B. Complex
   C. Glucose
   D. Dextrose

3. _____ are the body's main energy source.
   A. Lipids
   B. Proteins
   C. Minerals
   D. Carbohydrates

4. What allows glucose, or blood sugar, to travel throughout the body for energy use?
   A. Fiber
   B. Insulin
   C. Micronutrients
   D. Macronutrients

5. What is the chemical process that causes unsaturated fats to spoil?
   A. Digestion
   B. Oxidation
   C. Absorption
   D. Hydrogenation

6. The process that alters the physical properties of fats and makes them stay fresh longer is called
   A. digestion.
   B. absorption.
   C. evaporation.
   D. hydrogenation.

7. Butter, lard, and meat are sources of which type of fat?
   A. Saturated
   B. Cholesterol
   C. Monounsaturated
   D. Polyunsaturated

8. Which nutrient is needed to build new cells and repair injured ones?
   A. Lipids
   B. Proteins
   C. Vitamins
   D. Minerals

9. Macaroni and cheese is an example of which type of protein?
   A. Complete
   B. Incomplete
   C. Complementary
   D. Uncomplementary

10. Chemical compounds found in food that are needed for regulating metabolic processes are called
    A. hormones.
    B. vitamins.
    C. amino acids.
    D. fatty acids.

11. Sodium and _____ are needed for maintaining the body's water balance.
    A. zinc
    B. iron
    C. calcium
    D. potassium

12. Which mineral is essential for replenishing red blood cells?
    A. Zinc
    B. Iron
    C. Iodine
    D. Phosphorus

13. What percentage of the human body is water by weight?
    A. 35 to 45
    B. 45 to 55
    C. 55 to 65
    D. 65 to 75

14. The process of breaking down food into its simplest parts so that it can be absorbed is called
    A. oxidation.
    B. digestion.
    C. evaporation.
    D. hydrogenation.

15. The daily nutrient standards established by the U.S. government are called

    A. Adequate Intakes.

    B. the Food Guide Pyramid.

    C. Dietary Guidelines for Americans.

    D. Recommended Dietary Allowances.

16. Which type of vegetarian consumes vegetarian items plus dairy products and eggs?

    A. Vegan

    B. Ovo

    C. Lacto

    D. Lacto-ovo

17. What condition occurs when the body does not get enough nutrients?

    A. Anemia

    B. Anorexia

    C. Diabetes

    D. Malnutrition

18. What is the condition in which the body cannot regulate blood sugar properly?

    A. Anemia

    B. Anorexia

    C. Diabetes

    D. Malnutrition

19. What is the proper temperature range for a storeroom?

    A. 10°F to 30°F

    B. 30°F to 50°F

    C. 50°F to 70°F

    D. 70°F to 90°F

20. Chemicals that kill insects and other plant pests are called

    A. hormones.

    B. antibiotics.

    C. pesticides.

    D. herbicides.

21. What nutrients are lost when meat is cooked too long?

    A. Iron and water

    B. Protein and vitamin B_{12}

    C. Thiamin and vitamin B_6

    D. Vitamin C and phosphorous

22. What are proteins made of?

    A. Fiber

    B. Starch

    C. Fatty acids

    D. Amino acids

23. Energy from food is measured in units called

    A. calories.

    B. nutrients.

    C. fatty acids.

    D. amino acids.

24. What substance found in food promotes digestive health and regularity?

    A. Fat

    B. Fiber

    C. Sugar

    D. Starch

25. Baked potatoes, cereal, and honey are good sources of

    A. fat.

    B. protein.

    C. minerals.

    D. carbohydrates.

26. What is the only source of energy for the brain and nervous system?
   A. Fiber
   B. Protein
   C. Glucose
   D. Insulin

27. Which organ produces insulin?
   A. Liver
   B. Kidney
   C. Pancreas
   D. Gall bladder

28. Where in the body is cholesterol made?
   A. Heart
   B. Liver
   C. Kidney
   D. Pancreas

29. Sunflower, soybean, and fish oils are sources of which type of fat?
   A. Saturated
   B. Cholesterol
   C. Monosaturated
   D. Polyunsaturated

30. Proteins provide the building blocks in the form of
   A. fiber.
   B. starch.
   C. fatty acids.
   D. amino acids.

31. How many amino acids can be found in food?
   A. 9
   B. 20
   C. 27
   D. 35

32. Which minerals help build strong bones and teeth?
   A. Iron and zinc
   B. Potassium and sodium
   C. Magnesium and copper
   D. Calcium and phosphorous

33. Red beans and rice combined is an example of a _____ protein.
   A. complete
   B. complex
   C. incomplete
   D. complementary

34. Which type of vegetarian consumes only grains, legumes, vegetables, fruit, nuts, and seeds?
   A. Vegan
   B. Ovo
   C. Lacto
   D. Lacto-ovo

35. Vegans need to supplement their diet with a source of which vitamin?
   A. A
   B. B
   C. C
   D. D

36. According to the U.S. Centers for Disease Control and Prevention, what percentage of U.S. children and teens aged 6 to 19 are obese?
   A. 8
   B. 16
   C. 24
   D. 32

37. What condition causes the bones to gradually lose their minerals and become weak and fragile?
    A. Obesity
    B. Diabetes
    C. Osteoporosis
    D. Cardiovascular disease

38. Which type of disease affects the heart and blood vessels and combined is the number one leading cause of death in the United States?
    A. Cancer
    B. Diabetes
    C. Cardiovascular
    D. Osteoporosis

39. Products that have been produced without pesticides or synthetic fertilizers are called
    A. local.
    B. organic.
    C. conventional.
    D. genetically modified.

40. Chemicals that aid the body in fighting or preventing diseases are called
    A. fiber.
    B. additives.
    C. anthocyanins.
    D. phytochemicals.

Short Answer

1. _____ carbohydrates contain one or two sugars.

2. _____ fiber does not dissolve in water.

3. _____ is a white, waxy substance that helps the body carry out its many processes.

4. Vitamins A, D, E, and K are _____-soluable vitamins.

5. Plants or animals whose genetic makeup has been altered are known as _____.

Essay

1. Explain why water is so important to the body. What are other sources of water that are consumed during a day?

2. Discuss the importance of vitamins in the diet.

3. Discuss the ways to prepare fruit and vegetables while retaining nutrients.

Chapter 3
Cost Control

True/False

_____ 1. Prior to service, managers should taste each item to ensure it meets the operation's standard.

_____ 2. Poor storage procedures and facilities can greatly increase food costs due to waste and increased labor costs.

_____ 3. Revenue is the price an operation pays out in the purchasing and preparation of its products or the providing of its service.

_____ 4. Total food cost percentage is the relationship between sales and the cost of food to achieve those sales.

_____ 5. The service staff is the primary sales tool in most restaurant and foodservice operations.

Multiple Choice

1. The main categories of cost are food, beverage, labor, and
   A. fixed.
   B. variable.
   C. overhead.
   D. controllable.

2. Which category of cost includes rent and gas/electricity?
   A. Food
   B. Labor
   C. Beverage
   D. Overhead

3. It is common for operating budgets to be prepared
   A. daily.
   B. weekly.
   C. monthly.
   D. yearly.

4. What is the formula for calculating average sales per customer?
   A. Total number of customers divided by the total dollar sales
   B. Total dollar sales divided by the total number of customers
   C. Total dollar sales multiplied by the total number of customers
   D. Total dollar sales divided by the average number of customers

5. A record of the number of portions of every item sold on a menu is called a
   A. sales history.
   B. receiving sheet.
   C. production sheet.
   D. profit-and-loss report.

6. Which document lists all menu items that are going to be prepared for a given date?
   A. Purchase order
   B. Master schedule
   C. Receiving sheet
   D. Production sheet

7. Which menu pricing method divides the total revenue by the number of seats, average seat turnover, and days open in one year?
   A. Average check
   B. Straight markup
   C. Contribution margin
   D. Food cost percentage

8. A compilation of sales and cost information for a specific period of time is presented in a(n)
   A. balance sheet.
   B. operating budget.
   C. profit-and-loss report.
   D. statement of cash flows.

9. Another name for a profit-and-loss report is a(n)
   A. balance sheet.
   B. operating budget.
   C. income statement.
   D. statement of cash flows.

10. What information is found at the bottom of the income statement?
    A. Net earnings
    B. Total expenses
    C. Retained earnings
    D. Total cost of sales

11. An income statement shows an operation's
    A. assets and liabilities.
    B. cost of goods sold and revenue.
    C. cash and assets over a period of time.
    D. sales, cost of sales, and profit or loss over a period of time.

12. The physical inventory at the beginning of a given period is called _____ inventory.
    A. opening
    B. closing
    C. perpetual
    D. operational

13. What is the formula for calculating food cost percentage?
    A. Total revenue ÷ Sales
    B. Total food cost ÷ Sales
    C. Total sales ÷ Revenue
    D. Total food cost ÷ Revenue

14. A restaurant's total food cost for April was $1,500 and its sales were $6,000. What is the food cost percentage?
    A. 10
    B. 25
    C. 60
    D. 75

15. The form that shows how much product should be produced by the kitchen during a given meal period is called a(n)

   A. purchase order.

   B. receiving sheet.

   C. production sheet.

   D. food production chart.

16. The contribution margin represents a menu item's profits in relation to

   A. its cost.

   B. its price.

   C. overall profits.

   D. its portion size.

17. Which menu pricing method multiplies raw food costs by a predetermined fraction?

   A. Average check

   B. Straight markup

   C. Contribution margin

   D. Food cost percentage

18. A restaurant wants a 30 percent food cost percentage on all menu items. If spaghetti and meatballs costs $2.95 per portion, how should it be priced (round up)?

   A. $6.75

   B. $8.85

   C. $9.85

   D. $10.20

19. A restaurant sells baked ziti at a 50 percent markup. If the menu item costs $3, what is the selling price?

   A. $3.75

   B. $4.50

   C. $5.25

   D. $6.00

20. If a gallon of tomato sauce costs $12 and yields 60 portions, what is the standard portion cost?

   A. $0.20

   B. $0.33

   C. $0.50

   D. $.072

21. The portion of dollars that a particular menu item contributes to overall profits is called the

   A. fixed cost.

   B. overhead costs.

   C. contribution margin.

   D. total food costs percentage.

22. If a quick-service line cook overcooks a batch of chicken fingers that yields 20 servings at $5 a serving, what is the revenue lost?

   A. $25.00

   B. $50.00

   C. $75.00

   D. $100.00

23. A chart that shows employees' names and the days and times they are to work is called a(n)

   A. crew schedule.

   B. business plan.

   C. master schedule.

   D. employee production chart.

24. The best time for a restaurant or foodservice operation to receive deliveries is

   A. once a month.

   B. during meal periods.

   C. when business is slow.

   D. when business is busy.

25. How often should fresh fish be delivered?
    A. Every hour
    B. Every day
    C. Every other day
    D. Every week

26. How often should dry- or wet-aged meat be ordered and delivered?
    A. Every day
    B. Two times a week
    C. Once a week
    D. Biweekly

27. The document from a vendor that lists such details as items purchased, date of order, purchaser, and sales price is called a(n)
    A. invoice.
    B. purchase order.
    C. receiving sheet.
    D. inventory record.

28. Which inventory method assumes that stock has been rotated during the month?
    A. FIFO
    B. LIFO
    C. Latest purchase price
    D. Weighted average purchase price

29. An operation has 22 bottles of ketchup in inventory and each bottle costs $3.50. What is the total value of the bottled ketchup?
    A. $15.90
    B. $35.00
    C. $50.00
    D. $77.00

30. A restaurant's food costs for a month were $12,600 and its food cost percentage was 30 percent. How much did the restaurant earn in sales?
    A. $3,780
    B. $18,000
    C. $36,000
    D. $42,000

31. When management wants to minimize the value of the closing inventory, which method should be used?
    A. LIFO
    B. Actual purchase price
    C. Latest purchase price
    D. Weighted average purchase price

32. The amount of sales an operation is doing for a given time period is called
    A. price point.
    B. fixed costs.
    C. business volume.
    D. contribution margin.

33. A lease and utilities can be classified as what cost?
    A. Fixed
    B. Variable
    C. Controllable
    D. Noncontrollable

34. The cost of a food item is incurred when the item is
    A. ordered.
    B. budgeted.
    C. purchased.
    D. consumed.

35. The primary selling tool in most restaurants is the
    A. menu.
    B. decor.
    C. service.
    D. manager.

36. Which closing inventory method multiplies the number of units of each item by the most recent price paid for the item?
    A. Actual purchase price
    B. Last in, first out (LIFO)
    C. Latest purchase price (FIFO)
    D. Weighted average purchase price

37. What is the formula to calculate the average sales per customer?
    A. Total dollar sales ÷ Total food cost
    B. Total number of covers ÷ Total food cost
    C. Total dollar sales ÷ Total number of covers
    D. Total number of covers ÷ Total dollar sales

38. A restaurant has a food cost percentage of 45 percent. This means that its food cost is 45 percent of
    A. total costs.
    B. total sales.
    C. labor costs.
    D. overhead costs.

39. Foodservice managers plan their financial activities by preparing
    A. budgets.
    B. directives.
    C. work schedules.
    D. daily food cost sheets.

40. Income from the sale of food items is called
    A. expenses.
    B. revenue.
    C. fixed cost.
    D. food cost percentage.

Short Answer

1. Most operations can run historical sales and production reports from their ____ _____.

2. _____ _____ companies are one-stop shops that provide equipment, food, and supplies.

3. _____ represents the dollar value of a food product in storage and can be expressed in terms of units, values, or both.

4. The _____ method is used to cost an ingredient at the purchase price before any trim or waste is taken into account.

5. A(n) _____ is the portion of dollars that a particular menu item contributes to overall profits.

Essay

1. Explain how the menu reflects labor costs.

2. Explain why forecasting is important to a restaurant or foodservice operation.

3. List the causes of high food cost.

Chapter 4
Salads and Garnishing

True/False

_____ 1. Mayonnaise is the most stable and thickest emulsified dressing.

_____ 2. Most dips become thicker as they are held in the refrigerator.

_____ 3. Vinaigrettes are thicker dressings used on heartier lettuces.

_____ 4. Ingredients for a composed salad should be tossed together.

_____ 5. The four basic parts of any salad are the base, body, garnish, and dressing.

Multiple Choice

1. What is the most popular American lettuce?
   A. Bibb
   B. Boston
   C. Iceberg
   D. Romaine

2. Which salad green, also known as frisée, has a slightly bitter flavor?
   A. Arugula
   B. Radicchio
   C. Napa cabbage
   D. Curly endive

3. Which type of lettuce is the essential ingredient in Caesar salad?
   A. Leaf
   B. Boston
   C. Iceberg
   D. Romaine

4. Which part of the salad is made up of a layer of greens that line the plate or bowl in which the salad is served?
   A. Base
   B. Body
   C. Garnish
   D. Dressing

5. Which part of the salad enhances its appearance while also complementing the overall taste?
   A. Base
   B. Body
   C. Garnish
   D. Dressing

6. Which salad vegetable has a long stalk, mild flavor, and crisp texture?
   A. Beet
   B. Celery
   C. Radish
   D. Scallion

7. A chef's salad is an example of what type of salad?
   A. Fruit
   B. Green
   C. Bound
   D. Combination

8. Which salad type stimulates the appetite and is light enough for the first course?
   A. Appetizer
   B. Main course
   C. Intermezzo
   D. Accompaniment

9. A small portion of potato salad is a type of _____ salad.
   A. main
   B. appetizer
   C. intermezzo
   D. accompaniment

10. Which salad is intended to be a palate cleanser after a rich dinner and before dessert?
    A. Main
    B. Appetizer
    C. Intermezzo
    D. Accompaniment

11. Loose salad greens should be stored at a temperature range between
    A. 29°F to 35°F.
    B. 36°F to 41°F.
    C. 42°F to 47°F.
    D. 48°F to 55°F.

12. Unopened produce can be stored for _____ days.
    A. 1 to 3
    B. 4 to 6
    C. 7 to 9
    D. 10 to 12

13. Pasta salad is an example of which type of salad?
    A. Bound
    B. Green
    C. Vegetable
    D. Combination

14. Raw _____ and papaya should never be added to gelatin salad.
    A. pears
    B. apples
    C. peaches
    D. pineapple

15. What is the standard recipe for a basic vinaigrette?
    A. 1 part oil, 1 part vinegar
    B. 2 parts oil, 1 part vinegar
    C. 3 parts oil, 1 part vinegar
    D. 3 parts oil, 2 parts vinegar

16. Which type of oil must be disclosed on the menu because of allergies?
    A. Corn
    B. Canola
    C. Peanut
    D. Soybean

17. Which type of oil has a good omega-3, fatty acid profile?
    A. Corn
    B. Canola
    C. Safflower
    D. Cottonseed

18. Which vinegar is made from apples?
    A. Wine
    B. Cider
    C. Sherry
    D. Balsamic

19. An ingredient that can permanently bind unlike ingredients is called a
    A. colloid.
    B. solution.
    C. suspension.
    D. emulsifier.

20. Which type of dressing are Russian and Thousand Island?
    A. Vinaigrette
    B. Mayonnaise
    C. Mayonnaise-based
    D. Emulsified vinaigrette

21. Which condiment is a common addition to mayonnaise dressings?
    A. Relish
    B. Mustard
    C. Ketchup
    D. Horseradish

22. What is the main ingredient in guacamole?
    A. Peppers
    B. Tomatoes
    C. Chickpeas
    D. Avocados

23. The main ingredient in hummus is
    A. tomatoes.
    B. lime juice.
    C. chickpeas.
    D. avocados.

24. Which special wine vinegar is aged in wooden barrels?
    A. Cider
    B. White
    C. Balsamic
    D. Tarragon

25. Which potato dish is baked with cream, garlic, and cheese?
    A. Latkes
    B. Lyonnaise
    C. Duchesse
    D. Dauphinoise

26. What two ingredients do you need to make frosted grapes?
    A. Water and sugar
    C. Sugar and lemon
    D. Water and molasses
    B. Honey and lemon juice

27. For cucumber fans, use a _____ knife to score the cucumber vertically from end to end.
    A. chef's
    B. fillet
    C. channel
    D. scimitar

28. A bouquet of vegetables used as a garnish is called a
    A. jardiniere.
    B. printaniere.
    C. provençale.
    D. bouquetière.

29. A garnish of carrots, turnips, onions, and celery cut into uniform slices is called
    A. crécy.
    B. vichy.
    C. fermiere.
    D. printaniere.

30. A garnish of cauliflower is called
    A. vichy.
    B. clamart.
    C. dubarry.
    D. lyonnaise.

31. A garnish of onions is called
    A. doria.
    B. clamart.
    C. lyonnaise.
    D. parmentier.

32. The best way to clean salad greens is to
    A. shake them.
    B. soak them in water.
    C. dip them in and out of water.
    D. wipe them with a damp cloth.

33. What ingredient holds a bound salad together?
    A. Cream
    B. Egg yolks
    C. Olive oil
    D. Mayonnaise

34. To prevent fruit cut for a salad from discoloring, coat or sprinkle the fruit with
    A. water.
    B. sugar.
    C. lemon juice.
    D. vegetable oil.

35. If chicken is served Florentine, it is served with
    A. carrots.
    B. spinach.
    C. tomatoes.
    D. mushrooms.

36. Chicken and potato salads are examples of a _____ salad.
    A. bound
    B. vegetable
    C. composed
    D. combination

37. Coleslaw is an example of a _____ salad.
    A. bound
    B. vegetable
    C. composed
    D. combination

38. Which type of salad is grilled chicken Caesar salad?
    A. Starter
    B. Main course
    C. Intermezzo
    D. Accompaniment

39. Which type of salad is small and served along with the main meal?
    A. Fruit
    B. Dessert
    C. Intermezzo
    D. Accompaniment

40. Which type of salad is a Waldorf salad?
    A. Fruit
    B. Dessert
    C. Appetizer
    D. Accompaniment

Short Answer

1. _____ enhances the appearance of the salad while also complementing the overall taste.

2. The two types of green salad are tossed and _____.

3. A(n) _____ is a temporary mixture of ingredients that eventually separates back into its unique parts.

4. _____ dressings are thick and coat salad ingredients more heavily.

5. _____ can be served hot or cold and as an accompaniment to other foods.

Essay

1. Compare and contrast the differences in a dip and a dressing.

2. Compare the differences between a tossed salad and a composed salad.

3. Discuss the purpose of garnishes.

Chapter 5
Purchasing and Inventory

True/False

_____ 1. Purchasing lower- or inconsistent-quality food items can quickly lead to the failure of an operation.

_____ 2. Most managers try to keep daily food cost sheets at or below 33 percent.

_____ 3. Nonperishable products are food products sold or distributed in a form that will spoil or decay within a limited period of time.

_____ 4. The temperature of the storeroom should be between 60°F and 80°F.

_____ 5. Gross profit is the difference between the total cost of food and the cost of goods issued during a period.

Multiple Choice

1. The amount of funds available to a restaurant or foodservice operation at any given time is called
   A. net profit.
   B. cash position.
   C. gross receipts.
   D. contribution margin.

2. The flow of food to an operation is called the
   A. vendor path.
   B. retail channel.
   C. intermediary path.
   D. channel of distribution.

3. The three main layers in the channel of distribution are primary sources, intermediary sources, and
   A. vendors.
   B. retailers.
   C. distillers.
   D. wholesalers.

4. Which channel of distribution includes the farmers and ranchers who raise produce and livestock?
   A. Primary source
   B. Secondary source
   C. Tertiary source
   D. Intermediary source

5. The company that buys food items from a farmer and then resells those same food items to a retailer is known as a(n)
   A. distiller.
   B. manufacturer.
   C. primary source.
   D. intermediary source.

6. Furniture, fixtures, and equipment (FFE) are considered
   A. current assets.
   B. intangible assets.
   C. inventory expenses.
   D. capital expenditures.

7. The use of money for future profit is called
   A. profit.
   B. capital.
   C. revenue.
   D. investment.

8. The type of service that includes painting and carpeting and helps keep an operation in good shape is called
   A. utilities.
   B. support.
   C. technology.
   D. maintenance.

9. Which type of service includes garbage removal and flower services?
   A. Utilities
   B. Support
   C. Technology
   D. Maintenance

10. Wholesalers, distributors, and suppliers are all _____ in the channel of distribution.
    A. buyers
    B. retailers
    C. primary sources
    D. intermediary sources

11. Price savings created when a buyer purchases bulk quantities of food instead of individually portioned servings is called _____ value.
    A. time
    B. form
    C. place.
    D. service

12. Assets that an operation has at its disposal are called
    A. capital.
    B. revenue.
    C. gross profit.
    D. cash position.

13. A notice of a price that a supplier gives to a buyer during the purchasing process is called a
    A. bid.
    B. spec.
    C. quote.
    D. invoice.

14. Money or other goods received by a person in exchange for purchasing from a specific vendor is called a
    A. pay off.
    B. bribe.
    C. kickback.
    D. hush money.

15. Which purchasing document describes in detail the characteristics of products and services that an operation wants to buy?
    A. Purchase order
    B. Inventory sheet
    C. Specifications form
    D. Requisition form

16. Which product specification identifies how an item has been processed before being packaged?
    A. Sizing
    B. Packaging
    C. Market form
    D. Intended use

17. Which document do buyers and managers use to forecast their buying needs?
    A. Purchase order
    B. Inventory sheet
    C. Production record
    D. Requisition form

18. Which production record lists all menu items that the chefs will prepare on a given day?
    A. Purchase order
    B. Inventory sheet
    C. Production sheet
    D. Requisition form

19. Production sheets are usually prepared by the
    A. chef.
    B. buyer.
    C. supplier.
    D. manager.

20. This term describes when a restaurant or foodservice operation runs out of an item in the kitchen.
    A. Stockout
    B. Blank order
    C. Overproduction
    D. Underproduction

21. If a restaurant's daily food cost is $550 and total sales are $1,475, what is its daily food cost percentage?
    A. 27
    B. 37
    C. 47
    D. 57

22. A manager who wants to know how popular a menu item is over the course of a month would look at the
    A. production sheet.
    B. sales mix record.
    C. production record.
    D. daily food cost sheet.

23. The ideal amount of inventory items that an operation should have at all times is called
    A. par value.
    B. par stock.
    C. periodic inventory.
    D. perpetual inventory.

24. A legally binding written document that details exactly what the buyer is ordering from the vendor is called a(n)
   A. invoice.
   B. receiving sheet.
   C. purchase order.
   D. requisition form.

25. What form does a manager need to complete to purchase a new piece of equipment?
   A. Purchase order
   B. Receiving sheet
   C. Requisition form
   D. Product specification

26. The price that retailers pay for the convenience of selecting the time of delivery from suppliers is called _____ value.
   A. form
   B. time
   C. place
   D. service

27. The convenience of buying food items in bulk instead of in ready-to-use portions is known as _____ value.
   A. form
   B. time
   C. place
   D. service

28. Delivering fresh lobsters from Cape Cod to a market in Wichita, Kansas, is more expensive than delivering the lobsters to a market in New York. This is an example of _____ value.
   A. form
   B. time
   C. place
   D. service

29. The process of inspecting, accepting, and, in some cases, rejecting deliveries of goods and services is called
   A. storing.
   B. issuing.
   C. receiving.
   D. pilfering.

30. If an item is rejected at delivery, what form should the receiver complete?
   A. Invoice
   B. Credit memo
   C. Purchase order
   D. Receiving sheet

31. At what temperature should live shellfish be stored?
   A. 32°F
   B. 41°F
   C. 45°F
   D. 55°F

32. What is the humidity level for most fruits and vegetables?
   A. 55% to 65%
   B. 65% to 75%
   C. 75% to 85%
   D. 85% to 95%

33. Store dry food away from walls and at least _____ inches off of the floor.

    A. 3

    B. 6

    C. 9

    D. 12

34. A record of all goods that a restaurant or foodservice operation has on hand both in storage and in the kitchen prep area is called a(n)

    A. invoice.

    B. inventory.

    C. purchase order.

    D. production record.

35. Which type of inventory system relies on the use of inventory cards to record incoming and outgoing food items?

    A. Invoice

    B. Periodic

    C. Perpetual

    D. Production

36. Which type of inventory system records items when they are received and then when they are used up?

    A. Invoice

    B. Periodic

    C. Perpetual

    D. Production

37. The official procedure that employees use when taking an item out of the storeroom and putting it into production is called

    A. issuing.

    B. storing.

    C. pilfering.

    D. receiving.

38. A buyer must place an order for ketchup. Par stock is 12 cases, 5 cases are in stock, and 2 cases will be used before delivery. How many cases should the buyer order?

    A. 6

    B. 7

    C. 8

    D. 9

39. Items that are in constant demand are called

    A. stock.

    B. staples.

    C. inventory.

    D. stockouts.

40. The amount of water moisture in the air or in a contained space such as a refrigerator is called

    A. dew point.

    B. humidity.

    C. evaporation.

    D. condensation.

Short Answer

1. _____ are independent business owners who buy the right to use a company's name, products, and logo.

2. Sales mix records show items that sell well, which are also called _____.

3. A(n) _____ is a number assigned to each inventory item that alerts the buyer that the item needs to be restocked by the next delivery.

4. _____ is the illegal taking of inventory items by employees for their personal use.

5. A(n) _____ shows the cost of using a convenience food product compared to the cost of making the item from scratch.

Essay

1. Define a product spec and list the parts usually included.

2. Define a make-or-buy analysis and how a buyer uses one.

3. Why is it important to keep accurate inventory records?

Chapter 6
Meat, Poultry, and Seafood

True/False

_____ 1. Dark meat is higher in calories and fat than light meat.

_____ 2. Full eyes are a sign that a fish is fresh.

_____ 3. When meat is done cooking, it should be cut right away.

_____ 4. Aging gives meat a light color and also makes it more expensive.

_____ 5. Roasting requires a longer cooking time because this method cooks the whole bird.

Multiple Choice

1. The highest quality USDA grade of beef is
   A. good.
   B. prime.
   C. select.
   D. choice.

2. The connective tissue that breaks down during long, slow, moist-heat cooking is called
   A. elastin.
   B. fibrous.
   C. adipose.
   D. collagen.

3. The connective tissue that connects the meat to the bone and will not break down during cooking is called
   A. elastin.
   B. fibrous.
   C. adipose.
   D. collagen.

4. The more time spent butchering a piece of meat, the
   A. less expensive it will be.
   B. more expensive it will be.
   C. less flavorful it will be.
   D. more flavorful it will be.

5. Thin, boneless cuts of meat that are lightly pounded are called
   A. scallops.
   B. noisettes.
   C. tenderloin.
   D. medallions.

6. Which fabrication technique cuts a piece of meat lengthwise, nearly in half, so that it opens out and lies flat?
   A. Filleting
   B. Trussing
   C. Trimming
   D. Butterflying

7. Small, round pieces of meat that are molded by wrapping them in cheesecloth are called
   A. scallops.
   B. noisettes.
   C. tenderloin.
   D. medallions.

8. Thin strips of meat used for sautéing are called
   A. émincés.
   B. noisettes.
   C. tenderloin.
   D. medallions.

9. In order for the muscles to relax, meat must be aged _____ hours.
   A. 4 to 20
   B. 20 to 48
   C. 48 to 72
   D. 72 to 96

10. Fresh meat must be delivered at a temperature of _____ or lower.
    A. 21°F
    B. 31°F
    C. 41°F
    D. 51°F

11. Which dry-heat cooking methods are best suited for chops and steaks?
    A. Baking and grilling
    B. Broiling and grilling
    C. Roasting and grilling
    D. Broiling and roasting

12. Which dry-heat cooking method is ideal for the tender cuts from a rib or tenderloin?
    A. Baking
    B. Grilling
    C. Broiling
    D. Roasting

13. Which cooking method is the best way to cook tougher cuts of meat?
    A. Frying
    B. Grilling
    C. Braising
    D. Sautéing

14. Marinating tends to make meat more
    A. lean.
    B. moist.
    C. chewy.
    D. well-done.

15. Meat is firmest when it is cooked
    A. rare.
    B. medium.
    C. medium-well.
    D. well-done.

16. What is the highest quality grade of poultry?
   A. A
   B. B
   C. C
   D. D

17. The process of tying a bird's wings and legs to its body is called
   A. filleting.
   B. trussing.
   C. trimming.
   D. butterflying.

18. Poultry should be cooked until it is well-done at a temperature of
   A. 155°F.
   B. 165°F.
   C. 175°F.
   D. 185°F.

19. Which cooking method is most suited for preparing mole poblano?
   A. Dry-heat
   B. Moist-heat
   C. Combination
   D. Dry-heat with oil

20. Which grade of seafood is marked with a stamp?
   A. A
   B. B
   C. C
   D. D

21. Which category includes fish that are oval and flat in shape, and have both eyes on the same side of the head?
   A. Flatfish
   B. Shellfish
   C. Roundfish
   D. Square fish

22. Mahi mahi and tuna are examples of
   A. flatfish.
   B. roundfish.
   C. crustaceans.
   D. cephalopods.

23. Which category of fish includes those with an outer shell but no backbone, and that live primarily in salt water?
   A. Finfish
   B. Flatfish
   C. Roundfish
   D. Shellfish

24. Which category includes shellfish that have an outer skeleton and jointed appendages?
   A. Finfish
   B. Mollusks
   C. Crustaceans
   D. Cephalopods

25. Which category of shellfish includes those with a single internal shell and tentacles?
   A. Finfish
   B. Mollusks
   C. Crustaceans
   D. Cephalopods

26. When only the viscera of a fish have been removed, the fish is called
   A. drawn.
   B. whole.
   C. filleted.
   D. dressed.

27. When a fish's viscera, scales, fins, and often its head are removed, it is called
    A. drawn.
    B. whole.
    C. filleted.
    D. dressed.

28. The process of removing a shrimp's digestive tract is called
    A. trussing.
    B. shucking.
    C. deveining.
    D. trimming.

29. How many days must shellstock identification tags be kept on file from the date the last shellfish was sold or served?
    A. 30
    B. 60
    C. 90
    D. 120

30. When poultry is done cooking, its juices should be
    A. red.
    B. pink.
    C. brown.
    D. clear.

31. When fish and seafood are cooked *en papillote*, they are cooked in
    A. a steamer.
    B. a stockpot.
    C. cheesecloth.
    D. parchment paper.

32. Which type of sausage is pepperoni?
    A. Fresh
    B. Frozen
    C. Dried or hard
    D. Smoked or cooked

33. Sausages are encased in
    A. cheesecloth.
    B. poultry skin.
    C. animal intestines.
    D. parchment paper.

34. A forcemeat made of white meat is called a(n)
    A. terrine.
    B. andouille.
    C. charcuterie.
    D. mousseline.

35. Kielbasa and andouille are examples of which type of sausage?
    A. Fresh
    B. Cured
    C. Pickled
    D. Smoked

36. A quenelle is a
    A. type of fresh sausage.
    B. forcemeat baked in dough.
    C. poached, dumpling-shaped forcemeat.
    D. forcemeat made of beef rather than pork.

37. Which method for cooking poultry retains the most nutrients?
    A. Boiling
    B. Steaming
    C. Simmering
    D. Deep-frying

38. When a cut of meat or poultry is barded, it is
    A. sliced very thin.
    B. marinated in the refrigerator.
    C. tied so it will cook evenly.
    D. covered with slices of fat.

39. The first step in trimming a tenderloin is to
A. trim the fat.
B. pound it flat.
C. truss the meat.
D. make a butterfly cut.

40. The tough membrane on meat is called
A. noisettes.
B. medallions.
C. silverskin.
D. scallions.

Short Answer

1. The amount of usable meat after the fat has been trimmed is called _____.

2. _____ is working with primal cuts of meat to customize them.

3. _____ cuts are ready for sale.

4. Forcemeat made of veal, poultry, or fish is called _____.

5. _____ is the lines of fat running throughout a piece of meat that enhance its flavor, tenderness, and juiciness.

Essay

1. Discuss how to properly store fresh meat.

2. Explain why it is important to check fish for freshness.

3. Identify the different varieties of forcemeat.

Chapter 7
Marketing

True/False

_____ 1. Personal selling is very expensive for restaurant and foodservice operations.

_____ 2. Point-of-sale displays include table tents and banners reminding customers of products and services.

_____ 3. The traditional P's of the marketing mix are product, price, promotion, and production.

_____ 4. Market segmentation is used within the restaurant and foodservice industry because it helps operations target their customers.

_____ 5. The contemporary marketing mix is a special marketing formula for the restaurant and foodservice industry.

Multiple Choice

1. For business purposes, a collection of people with similar, specific needs and wants is called a
   A. group.
   B. market.
   C. segment.
   D. community.

2. The process of communicating a business's messages to its market is called
   A. servicing.
   B. presenting.
   C. marketing.
   D. positioning.

3. All the food and services offered by an operation to a customer is an example of _____ mix.
   A. presentation
   B. communication
   C. product-service
   D. contemporary marketing

4. The use of location, decor, and theme to make the operation more pleasing to customers is an example of _____ mix.
   A. presentation
   B. communication
   C. product-service
   D. contemporary marketing

5. The way in which an operation tells its customers about its products and services is called _____ mix.
   A. presentation
   B. communication
   C. product-service
   D. contemporary marketing

6. The list of action steps necessary for an operation to sell a product or service is called a
   A. marketing plan.
   B. promotion mix.
   C. research report.
   D. mission statement.

7. Which part of a SWOT analysis identifies the factors outside the operation that could decrease revenues or increase costs?
   A. Strengths
   B. Weaknesses
   C. Opportunities
   D. Threats

8. Which market research method tries out a product for a limited time or with a limited group of people?
   A. Survey
   B. Sampling
   C. Experimental
   D. Observational

9. Which market research method involves watching how customers react in a natural setting toward a product?
   A. Survey
   B. Sampling
   C. Experimental
   D. Observational

10. Which market research method gathers information through telephone, e-mail, or tableside?
    A. Survey
    B. Sampling
    C. Experimental
    D. Observational

11. A small group of people expressing their opinions about a new product or service is called a
    A. survey.
    B. sampling.
    C. focus group.
    D. demographic analysis.

12. Breaking down a large market into smaller groups of similar individuals is called
    A. forecasting.
    B. positioning.
    C. market segmentation.
    D. unique selling proposition.

13. Which type of marketing treats everyone as having the same needs and wants?
    A. Mass
    B. Target
    C. Geographic
    D. Demographic

14. Which type of marketing treats people as different from each other and tries to make a focused appeal to a distinct group of customers?
    A. Mass
    B. Target
    C. Geographic
    D. Demographic

15. Which type of segmentation breaks down a large market into smaller groups of similar individuals?
    A. Market
    B. Benefit
    C. Lifestyle
    D. Demographic

16. Which market segmentation looks at the personal makeup of individuals—such as age, income, marital status, or education—in a given area?
    A. Benefit
    B. Lifestyle
    C. Geographic
    D. Demographic

17. Which market segmentation looks at factors such as where customers live and work?
    A. Benefit
    B. Lifestyle
    C. Geographic
    D. Demographic

18. Which type of market segmentation analyzes the heavy users of a product or service?
    A. Benefit
    B. Lifestyle
    C. Unique selling
    D. Product usage

19. Which market segmentation looks at the activities, hobbies, interests, and opinions of the target market?
    A. Lifestyle
    B. Geographic
    C. Demographic
    D. Product usage

20. Creating a specific identity for a product or service in the marketplace is called
    A. marketing.
    B. forecasting.
    C. positioning.
    D. segmenting.

21. Paying to present or promote an operation's products, services, or identity is called
    A. advertising.
    B. personal selling.
    C. public relations.
    D. direct marketing.

22. Limited, or short-term, incentives to entice customers to patronize an operation are known as
    A. advertising.
    B. personal selling.
    C. sales promotions.
    D. direct marketing.

23. The process by which an operation interacts with the community at large is called
    A. advertising.
    B. personal selling.
    C. public relations.
    D. direct marketing.

24. The first step in any marketing plan is to
    A. establish objectives.
    B. research the market.
    C. develop a market strategy.
    D. evaluate feedback from customers.

25. The mass mailing of coupons, menus, and advertising about a promotion to customers in a particular area is called
   A. service.
   B. signage.
   C. premium.
   D. direct mail.

26. Interacting with the people in the local area to create awareness of and trust for an operation is called
   A. advertising.
   B. personal selling.
   C. direct marketing.
   D. community relations.

27. A packet of information given to media representatives to answer questions they might have about a business or organization is called a
   A. publicity.
   B. press kit.
   C. press release.
   D. media vehicle.

28. Which type of menu prices each item separately?
   A. Limited
   B. Du jour
   C. Á la carte
   D. Table d'hôte

29. Which type of menu lists the menu items that are available on a particular day?
   A. Fixed
   B. Du jour
   C. Limited
   D. Prix fixe

30. Chefs or managers change the menu items after a certain period of time on which type of menu?
   A. Du jour
   B. Limited
   C. Cyclical
   D. California

31. A(n) _____ analysis is an analysis of the popularity and the profitability of a group of menu items.
   A. sales mix
   B. menu mix
   C. sales percentage
   D. contribution margin

32. The menu that offers few selections and is used often by quick-service restaurants and cafés is called
   A. fixed.
   B. limited.
   C. cyclical.
   D. California.

33. Which type of menu lists all meals available at any time of day and is often used by diners that are open 24 hours?
   A. Limited
   B. California
   C. Prix fixe
   D. Table d'hôte

34. The menu that offers a choice of appetizer, full entrée with sides, and a dessert for one price is called
   A. fixed.
   B. prix fixe.
   C. California.
   D. table d'hôte.

35. The menu similar to a prix fixe menu that bundles various elements into one package is called
    A. fixed.
    B. adjusted.
    C. California.
    D. table d'hôte.

36. Selling price minus the standard food cost equals
    A. menu mix.
    B. standard food cost.
    C. food cost percentage.
    D. contribution margin.

37. Which pricing method has managers mark up the costs according to a formula to obtain the selling price?
    A. Average check
    B. Set percentage
    C. Straight markup
    D. Contribution margin

38. Dividing the menu mix by the total number of items sold in a specific time period determines
    A. standard food cost.
    B. contribution margin.
    C. menu mix percentage.
    D. food cost percentage.

39. Which menu item classification has a high menu mix percentage and a low contribution margin?
    A. Dog
    B. Star
    C. Puzzle
    D. Plowhorse

40. Which menu item classification has a low menu mix percentage and a low contribution margin?
    A. Dog
    B. Star
    C. Puzzle
    D. Plowhorse

Short Answer

1. _____ is the attention an operation receives from the public.

2. A(n) _____ is a brief presentation of promotional information written to sound like a news article.

3. _____ is defined as the amount of money remaining for an operation after expenses, or costs, are paid.

4. _____ is the process of communicating a business's message to its market.

5. _____ refer to the ways in which researchers categorize or group people.

Essay

1. Explain why marketing is important in the restaurant and foodservice industry.

2. Discuss market segmentation: List and give examples.

3. Discuss market demand and how it is determined.

Chapter 8
Desserts and Baked Goods

True/False

_____ 1. Dough that is being proofed should be left to rise until it is 3 times its original size.

_____ 2. Bloom has no effect on the quality of chocolate.

_____ 3. Sourdough breads are leavened with a starter.

_____ 4. Soufflés are more stable than steamed puddings because they have a greater percentage of eggs and sugar in their batter.

_____ 5. Due to their high sugar content, cookies are best when they are baked in convection ovens.

Multiple Choice

1. Which ingredient makes baked goods moist, adds flavor, and keeps the baked item fresh?
   A. Gluten
   B. Leavener
   C. Thickener
   D. Shortening

2. Which ingredient used in baking causes the dough to rise?
   A. Gluten
   B. Leavener
   C. Thickener
   D. Shortening

3. Which type of wheat flour used to make breads is hard and has a little higher gluten level than typical bread flour?
   A. Cake
   B. Durum
   C. Semolina
   D. All-purpose

4. Which ingredient adds flavor and color to baked goods?
   A. Leavener
   B. Shortening
   C. Thickener
   D. Sweetener

5. Which type of leavener, used often in baking, is a microscopic fungus?
   A. Yeast
   B. Steam
   C. Baking soda
   D. Baking powder

6. The process of browning sugar under heat is called
   A. denaturing.
   B. fermentation.
   C. glutenization.
   D. caramelization.

7. Baking soda and baking powder are which type of leavener?
   A. Organic
   B. Physical
   C. Chemical
   D. Biological

8. Which baking ingredient determines the consistency of the finished product?
   A. Leavener
   B. Shortening
   C. Thickener
   D. Sweetener

9. Which ingredient provides moisture to the baked product and allows the gluten to develop properly?
   A. Flour
   B. Yeast
   C. Liquid
   D. Extract

10. French bread is a type of _____ dough.
    A. soft
    B. rich
    C. lean
    D. sponge

11. Which type of dough is made by adding shortening or tenderizing ingredients such as sugar, syrup, butter, eggs, milk, and cream?
    A. Soft
    B. Rich
    C. Lean
    D. Sponge

12. Allowing yeast dough to rise just before baking is called
    A. yeasting.
    B. kneading.
    C. proofing.
    D. portioning.

13. In which method for preparing quick bread and cake batters are the fat and sugar creamed together to produce a very fine crumb and a dense, rich texture?
    A. Creaming
    B. Foaming
    C. Two-stage
    D. Straight-dough

14. Corn bread and blueberry muffins are examples of quick breads made using the _____ method.
    A. creaming
    B. foaming
    C. two-stage
    D. straight-dough

15. Which method for preparing cake batters is used to make devil's food cake?
    A. Creaming
    B. Foaming
    C. Two-stage
    D. Straight-dough

16. Which type of icing has a shiny, nonsticky coating when dried?
    A. Foam
    B. Fondant
    C. Ganache
    D. Buttercream

17. What is the main ingredient in soufflés?
    A. Sugar
    B. Shortening
    C. All-purpose flour
    D. Beaten egg whites

18. Pie crust is made using _____ dough.
    A. 3-2-1
    B. phyllo
    C. foaming
    D. creaming

19. The procedure for preparing a prebaked pie shell is called
    A. par-baking.
    B. oven spring.
    C. fermentation.
    D. baking blind.

20. Which dough is used to make puff pastries?
    A. 3-2-1
    B. Phyllo
    C. Strudel
    D. Roll-in

21. Which dough is used most often to create cream puffs and éclairs?
    A. Phyllo
    B. Strudel
    C. Roll-in
    D. *Pâte à choux*

22. Which type of cookie includes chocolate chip and oatmeal?
    A. Bar
    B. Drop
    C. Sheet
    D. Rolled

23. Peanut butter cookies are an example of a _____ cookie.
    A. drop
    B. sheet
    C. molded
    D. rolled

24. Cocoa butter that has been flavored and sweetened is called
    A. cocoa powder.
    B. white chocolate.
    C. chocolate liquor.
    D. bittersweet chocolate.

25. How should chocolate be stored?
    A. Frozen
    B. In refrigeration
    C. At room temperature
    D. In a cool, dry, well-ventilated area

26. Chocolate is tempered so that it will
    A. melt evenly.
    B. taste bittersweet.
    C. have a neutral flavor.
    D. have less fat and fewer calories.

27. What should you do if chocolate becomes grainy or scorched during tempering?
    A. Add more liquid.
    B. Add more chocolate.
    C. Reduce the heat.
    D. Discard the chocolate.

28. During the tempering process, to what temperature should the chocolate be heated?
    A. 87°F
    B. 92°F
    C. 105°F
    D. 120°F

29. A light, vanilla-flavored custard sauce made from milk, egg yolks, and sugar is called
    A. pastry cream.
    B. Bavarian cream.
    C. sabayon sauce.
    D. crème anglaise.

30. A type of custard made by combining vanilla sauce, gelatin, and whipped cream is called
    A. sabayon.
    B. pastry cream.
    C. Bavarian cream.
    D. crème anglaise.

31. A dense custard used as the filling for pastries and éclairs is called
    A. sabayon.
    B. pastry cream.
    C. Bavarian cream.
    D. crème anglaise.

32. In baking, flour always has a proportion of what percentage?
    A. 25
    B. 50
    C. 75
    D. 100

33. A basic pie dough is called 3-2-1 dough because it contains
    A. 3 parts fat, 2 parts flour, 1 part water.
    B. 3 parts flour, 2 parts fat, 1 part water.
    C. 3 parts water, 2 parts flour, 1 part water.
    D. 3 parts fat, 2 parts water, 1 part flour.

34. Which type of dough is used to make baklava?
    A. Pie
    B. Phyllo
    C. Foaming
    D. Sourdough

35. Which method is used to prepare products with a more refined crumb and dense, rich texture?
    A. Two-stage
    B. Foaming
    C. Creaming
    D. Straight mix

36. Which method produces cakes with the lightest texture?
    A. Two-stage
    B. Foaming
    C. Creaming
    D. Straight mix

37. Cocoa beans that have been crushed into a paste are called
    A. blooms.
    B. cocoa powder.
    C. chocolate liquor.
    D. tempered chocolate.

38. Belle Hélène is an example of a
    A. sherbet.
    B. custard.
    C. poached fruit.
    D. dessert sauce.

39. Sabayon is made with egg yolks, sugar, and
    A. butter.
    B. gelatin.
    C. Marsala wine.
    D. confectioner's sugar.

40. Which type of cookie includes blondies?
    A. Bar
    B. Sheet
    C. Icebox
    D. Molded

Short Answer

1. A white coating that sometimes appears on the surface of chocolate is called _____.

2. Standardized recipes for bakery products are called _____.

3. _____ are the basis of all cocoa products.

4. A(n) _____ is an elegant, rich, many-layered cake often filled with buttercream or jam.

5. A(n) _____ is a fruit sauce made from fresh berries or other fruits.

Essay

1. Compare and contrast lean and rich doughs.

2. Discuss the different types of cookies.

3. Discuss the differences between sorbet and sherbet.

Chapter 9
Sustainability in the Restaurant and Foodservice Industry

True/False

_____ 1. To conserve water, restaurant and foodservice operations should only serve water to customers if they request it.

_____ 2. Half of all water use in a restaurant occurs in the kitchen.

_____ 3. Meat and fish bones are ideal for composting.

_____ 4. In aquaculture, open systems require much more management than do closed systems, and they frequently require more energy usage as well.

_____ 5. Organic foods have been produced without pesticides or synthetic fertilizers.

Multiple Choice

1. The U.S. government agency that was founded in 1970 that has a mission to protect human health and the environment is the
   A. Environmental Protection Agency.
   B. U.S. Department of Energy.
   C. U.S. EPA Green Power Partnership.
   D. Food and Agriculture Organization.

2. The practice of meeting current resource needs without compromising the ability to accommodate future needs is called
   A. sustainability.
   B. conservation.
   C. preservation.
   D. reduction.

3. The practice of limiting the use of a resource is called
   A. sustainability.
   B. conservation.
   C. preservation.
   D. reduction.

4. The Earth's surface is covered with almost 75 percent water, but only _____ percent of that can be used by humans, either as groundwater or freshwater.
   A. 1
   B. 3
   C. 7
   D. 10

5. What percentage of the United States relies on groundwater to supply its households and businesses with water?
   A. 10
   B. 20
   C. 30
   D. 40

6. Approximately how many millions of gallons of freshwater are used each day in the United States?
   A. 175
   B. 250
   C. 350
   D. 425

7. Public water supply and treatment facilities in the United States consume about _____ billion kilowatt-hours per year.
   A. 36
   B. 56
   C. 76
   D. 96

8. Fuels that are formed from plant or animal remains buried deep in the earth are called
   A. biofuels.
   B. fossil fuels.
   C. natural gas.
   D. nuclear gas.

9. Which renewable energy source contains stored energy from the sun through photosynthesis?
   A. Wind
   B. Solar
   C. Biomass
   D. Geothermal

10. Which renewable energy source comes from heat inside the earth?
   A. Wind
   B. Solar
   C. Biomass
   D. Geothermal

11. Which type of renewable energy source converts energy to electricity using photovoltaics?
   A. Wind
   B. Solar
   C. Biomass
   D. Geothermal

12. In a restaurant or foodservice operation, which area uses the most energy?
   A. Lighting
   B. Refrigeration
   C. Heating/cooling
   D. Cooking equipment

13. An abandoned, polluted industrial site that can be repurposed for commercial business use is called a
    A. brownfield site.
    B. green building.
    C. brown building.
    D. greenfield site.

14. Food that customers did not eat, but that back-of-the-house staff prepared, cooked, cooled, and held safely is called _____ food.
    A. organic
    B. recycled
    C. repurposed
    D. composted

15. What type of environment is one in which food has been within the kitchen's control and has been kept safe from cross-contamination and time-temperature abuse?
    A. Open
    B. Closed
    C. Controlled
    D. Uncontrolled

16. Printing on both sides of paper is an example of which waste management effort?
    A. Reuse
    B. Reduce
    C. Recycle
    D. Reprocess

17. Accurate forecasting can help which waste management effort?
    A. Reuse
    B. Reduce
    C. Recycle
    D. Reprocess

18. Which waste management effort transforms waste into valuable resources?
    A. Reusing
    B. Reducing
    C. Recycling
    D. Reprocessing

19. Low-flow spray valves help to conserve water by
    A. adding air to the sprayer.
    B. recirculating water already sprayed.
    C. holding the water in a tank until ready to be used.
    D. reducing the amount of water coming out of the sprayer.

20. Sink aerators help to conserve water by
    A. recirculating steam.
    B. holding water in a tank.
    C. adding air to a water flow.
    D. reducing the amount of water coming out.

21. A natural form of recycling that occurs when organic material decomposes to form organic fertilizer is called
    A. reusing.
    B. reducing.
    C. composting.
    D. repurposing.

22. Food produced in the surrounding growing region is called a _____ source.
    A. local
    B. non-local
    C. regional
    D. community

23. What is the most consumed seafood in the United States?
    A. Tuna
    B. Shrimp
    C. Salmon
    D. Tilapia

24. The production of seafood under controlled conditions is called
    A. aquaculture.
    B. wild fishing.
    C. conservation.
    D. bottom trawling.

25. Aquaculture accounts for what percentage of seafood consumed globally?
    A. 30
    B. 40
    C. 50
    D. 60

26. The United States is responsible for the production of approximately _____ million pounds of seafood each year.
    A. 500
    B. 600
    C. 700
    D. 800

27. Which type of aquaculture system uses a natural body of water to produce seafood?
    A. Open
    B. Closed
    C. Controlled
    D. Uncontrolled

28. Which type of system on an aquaculture farm reconditions and reuses the water?
    A. Open
    B. Closed
    C. Controlled
    D. Uncontrolled

29. Coffee trees grow under taller rainforest trees using the _____ coffee method.
    A. sun
    B. shadow
    C. shade-grown
    D. roasted-grown

30. Foods that have been produced without pesticides or synthetic fertilizers are
    A. fresh.
    B. organic.
    C. hormone-free.
    D. conventional.

31. Hands should be washed in water at what temperature?
    A. 90°F
    B. 100°F
    C. 110°F
    D. 120°F

32. To use water efficiently, restaurant and foodservice operations should thaw food
    A. in coolers.
    B. in the microwave.
    C. on the counter.
    D. under running water.

33. To use water efficiently, restaurant and foodservice operations should scrape and soak dirty cookware and plates

    A. in standing water.

    B. under running water.

    C. in boiling water.

    D. in freezing water.

34. Turning off the lights when leaving a room is an example of _____ energy.

    A. recycling

    B. conserving

    C. sustaining

    D. repurposing

35. What percentage of the world's fish species have been fully fished, overfished, or depleted within the last 15 years?

    A. 35

    B. 50

    C. 65

    D. 75

36. Worldwide, coffee production accounts for approximately _____ million acres of farmland spread over 60 countries.

    A. 10

    B. 20

    C. 30

    D. 40

37. Which method of cleaning sidewalks and parking lots would best help to conserve resources?

    A. Using one bucket of water

    B. Watering with a hose

    C. Using a leaf blower

    D. Sweeping

38. A _____ adds air to a water flow, thus reducing water consumption.

    A. sink aerator

    B. connectionless steamer

    C. tankless water heater

    D. low-flow spray valve

39. The EPA reports that commercial buildings consume _____ percent of all electricity used in the United States.

    A. 44

    B. 54

    C. 64

    D. 74

40. When some species are being caught at a faster rate than they can reproduce it is called

    A. bycatch.

    B. trawling.

    C. overfishing.

    D. underfishing.

Short Answer

1. _____ is the practice of meeting current resource needs without compromising the ability to accommodate future needs.

2. A(n) _____ building is one that has been designed, built, renovated, or reused so that the structure conserves energy, uses resources more efficiently, and reduces the overall impact on the environment.

3. Operations can reduce total waste by reducing, reusing, and _____.

4. _____ is the production of seafood under controlled conditions.

5. _____ systems of aquaculture use a natural body of water to produce fish.

Essay

1. Why is water conservation important?

2. Determine ways a restaurant and foodservice operation can reduce.

3. What are the ways a restaurant and foodservice operation can conserve energy?

Chapter 10
Global Cuisine 1: The Americas

True/False

_____ 1. In Cal-Mex cuisine the meats are shredded, while in Tex-Mex cuisine the meats are generally ground.

_____ 2. The ancient Mexican diet was usually vegetarian, perhaps supplemented with seafood in the coastal regions.

_____ 3. Mexican cooking has influenced all cuisines because barbecue originated in this region.

_____ 4. Brazil introduced the Western world to citrus fruits, which were brought to the New World and grown in Portugal.

_____ 5. *Comales* used in Mexican cooking are made of cast-iron.

Multiple Choice

1. Who cultivated a diet called "Three Sisters," which consists of corn, beans, and squash?
   A. Iroquois
   B. Pilgrims
   C. Puritans
   D. Italians

2. A classic menu item that includes corned beef brisket, boiled potatoes, cabbage, and root vegetables is called
   A. jambalaya.
   B. shish kebab.
   C. low country broil.
   D. New England boiled dinner.

3. Blueberries, cranberries, and Concord grapes are staple fruits of what U.S. region?
   A. South
   B. Midwest
   C. Southwest
   D. Northwest

4. Which type of cuisine usually showcases simple, hearty dishes that make use of locally grown food?
   A. Southern
   B. Midwestern
   C. Northwestern
   D. Southwestern

5. Which people arrived in the Midwest in the 1700s and introduced the tradition of serving meals family style?
   A. Italians
   B. Germans
   C. Hungarians
   D. Scandinavians

6. What did the Scandinavians introduce to the Midwest?
   A. Lefse
   B. Pasties
   C. Goulash
   D. Sauerkraut

7. Which Southern cuisine was influenced by the American Indians, who taught European settlers to plant corn and introduced them to native squashes, plums, berries, greens, game, and seafood, including fish and oysters?
   A. Cajun
   B. Creole
   C. Tidewater
   D. Low country

8. Which cuisine began by blending French grand cuisine principles with the cooking techniques of enslaved Africans?
   A. Cajun
   B. Creole
   C. Tidewater
   D. Low country

9. Which style of cooking originated in the swamps and bayous of southwestern Louisiana?
   A. Cajun
   B. Creole
   C. Tidewater
   D. Low country

10. A hearty soup that is often made with trinity and shrimp and then thickened with brown roux and filé is called
    A. gumbo.
    B. andouille.
    C. jambalaya
    D. clam chowder.

11. Which Cajun dish is a spicy rice dish with chicken, andouille sausage, shrimp, crayfish, trinity, other vegetables, herbs, broth, and seasonings?
    A. Gumbo
    B. Andouille
    C. Jambalaya
    D. Clam chowder

12. Trinity is a form of mirepoix used in Cajun and Creole in which the carrots are replaced with
    A. okra.
    B. tomatoes.
    C. sweet potatoes.
    D. green bell peppers.

13. Salsa is a signature dish of which U.S. region?

    A. South

    B. Northeast

    C. Southwest

    D. Midwest

14. A style of cooking and presenting food that combines the ingredients and techniques of Asian and West Coast cuisines is called _____ cuisine.

    A. haute

    B. fusion

    C. classical

    D. nouveau

15. A tropical tree that produces seed pods containing beans that are ground to make cocoa powder is called

    A. yucca.

    B. cacao

    C. stevia.

    D. cassava.

16. A traditional Central American relish made from cabbage, onions, and carrots tossed in vinegar that is served as a condiment on many dishes is called

    A. *curtido.*

    B. *pupusa.*

    C. *gallo pinto.*

    D. *papa rellena.*

17. Where did barbecue originate?

    A. Caribbean

    B. United States

    C. Pacific Rim

    D. South America

18. A mix of salt pork, ham, onions, garlic, green peppers, jalapeño, tomato, oregano, and cilantro that is cooked slowly together and then used as a foundation in soups and stews is called

    A. jerk.

    B. *curtido.*

    C. *sofrito.*

    D. *pupusa.*

19. The staples of Bolivia are potatoes, rice, beans, and

    A. yucca.

    B. cacao.

    C. quinoa.

    D. bananas.

20. Which tropical fruit is a staple of Brazilian cuisine?

    A. Kiwi

    B. Quince

    C. Banana

    D. Pineapple

21. A mixture of citrus and fish that is a signature dish in Peru is called

    A. ceviche.

    B. guarana.

    C. churrasco.

    D. *gallo pinto.*

22. Creole and Cajun cooking are blends of what styles of cuisine?

    A. French, Indian, and Spanish.

    B. African, Indian, and Peruvian

    C. Spanish, French, Moroccan, and African

    D. American Indian, Spanish, French, and African

23. The flavors associated with the cuisine of the Southwestern United States are
    A. sweet and sour.
    B. salty and savory.
    C. smoky and spicy.
    D. sharp and bitter.

24. The flavors associated with the cuisine of the Northeastern United States are
    A. deep and rich.
    B. sweet and sour.
    C. simple and hearty.
    D. light and nutritious.

25. Cajun and Creole cuisines use a foundation of ingredients called the trinity, which consists of
    A. red peppers, onions, and carrots.
    B. celery, onions, and green peppers.
    C. scallions, carrots, and yellow peppers.
    D. garlic, orange peppers, and scallions.

26. A Cajun pork sausage that has a strong, smoky, garlicky taste is called
    A. gumbo.
    B. ceviche.
    C. andouille.
    D. jambalaya.

27. Which chef helped popularize fusion cuisine?
    A. Rick Bayless
    B. Emeril Lagasse
    C. Wolfgang Puck
    D. Alice Waters

28. The foods of Central America can be described as
    A. mild and earthy.
    B. salty and savory.
    C. smoky and spicy.
    D. light and nutritious.

29. A Central American dish that is a mix of white rice and black beans cooked separately and then fried together in coconut oil is called
    A. *sofrito.*
    B. *curtido.*
    C. andouille.
    D. *gallo pinto.*

30. Which plant is a staple crop in Africa, Asia, and South America?
    A. Yucca
    B. Cacao
    C. Cassava
    D. Anthurium

31. The technique used to cook a meat by adding spices and then roasting it over a smoky wood fire is called
    A. brining.
    B. grilling.
    C. barbecue.
    D. churrasco.

32. Roasting meat on skewers over fire is called
    A. grilling.
    B. stir-frying.
    C. barbecue.
    D. churrasco.

33. A thick, handmade, corn biscuit-like flat bread that is traditional to Central America is called a
    A. lefse.
    B. *curtido.*
    C. *sofrito.*
    D. *pupusa.*

34. In Jamaica, meat is seasoned with a spicy dry rub called
    A. allspice.
    B. jerk spice.
    C. Aztec rub.
    D. Creole rub.

35. The most notable variety of mole that is made with dried fruits and ancho chilis is called
    A. Mole Negro.
    B. Mole Verde.
    C. Mole Poblano.
    D. Mole Amarillo.

36. Which area is home to fusion cuisine?
    A. Northwest
    B. Southwest
    C. Midwest
    D. Pacific Rim

37. In Mexican cooking, comals are used as
    A. clay plates.
    B. glass bowls.
    C. ceramic pots.
    D. cast-iron pans.

38. The foods of Brazilian cuisine can be described as
    A. mild and earthy.
    B. salty and savory.
    C. savory and spicy.
    D. light and nutritious.

39. The British began to arrive in large numbers in the Northeast during the 1700s and brought meat pies called
    A. lefse.
    B. *curtido*.
    C. pasties.
    D. goulash.

40. In Cal-Mex cuisine of the Southwestern United States, the meats are
    A. diced.
    B. minced.
    C. ground.
    D. shredded.

Short Answer

1. _____ cuisine developed in the city of New Orleans in the homes of French and Spanish aristocrats.

2. _____ is a form of mirepoix that blends celery, onions, and green bell peppers.

3. The style of cooking and presenting food that combines the ingredients and techniques of Asian and West Coast cuisines is called _____ cuisine.

4. _____ is a traditional Central American relish originating in El Salvador that is made from cabbage, onions, and carrots tossed in vinegar.

5. _____ means sauce or mixture and can sometimes be used as a suffix on words to describe the sauce.

Essay

1. Describe the cuisine of the Pacific Rim.

2. Compare and contrast the flavor profiles of two U.S. regions.

3. Explain how Mexican cuisine has influenced American cuisine. Support your answer.

Chapter 11
Global Cuisine 2: Europe, the Mediterranean, the Middle East, and Asia

True/False

_____ 1. Catherine de Medici brought grand cuisine to France.

_____ 2. The Columbian Exchange brought many new foods to Spain, such as tomatoes, peppers, and beans.

_____ 3. The signature cooking methods of Morocco are *tagines* and *couscoussière*.

_____ 4. Garlic, tahini, and chickpeas are staples of Egyptian cuisine.

_____ 5. Canton cuisine refers to the elaborate and delicate specialties prepared for the elite members of the imperial court in Peking.

Multiple Choice

1. Which type of cuisine is characterized by highly refined dishes and a strictly disciplined brigade system?
   A. Grand
   B. Haute
   C. Classic
   D. Nouveau

2. The Alsatian specialty of engorged liver of a fattened goose or duck that is seared or poached, is called
   A. foie gras.
   B. cassoulet.
   C. duck confit.
   D. poulet de Bresse.

3. The French dish made from a blue-legged chicken of renowned tenderness and flavor is called
   A. foie gras.
   B. cassoulet.
   C. duck confit.
   D. poulet de Bresse.

4. Southwest France is renowned for which beans and meat dish?
   A. Foie gras
   B. Cassoulet
   C. Poulet de Bresse
   D. Jambon de Bayonne

5. Which European country is credited with creating the mother sauces?
   A. Italy
   B. Spain
   C. France
   D. Germany

6. The 2 major cooking fats of Italy are
   A. olive oil and butter.
   B. butter and soybean oil.
   C. margarine and egg yolks.
   D. clarified butter and canola oil.

7. Which country's food has been characterized as *la cucina povera*, the cuisine of poverty?
   A. Italy
   B. Spain
   C. France
   D. Germany

8. A Northern Italy dish that is an olive oil-based dipping sauce flavored with anchovy and garlic and then served warm with raw vegetables is called
   A. *brodetto.*
   B. *bagna cauda.*
   C. *bollito misto.*
   D. *vitello tonnato.*

9. Which dish is a hallmark of Genoa's cuisine?
   A. *Bollito misto*
   B. *Vitello tonnato*
   C. Pasta *con le sarde*
   D. *Bistecca alla Fiorentina*

10. Which group introduced Spain to citrus fruits, almonds, sugarcane, rice, saffron, and a wide variety of vegetables and spices?
    A. Arabs
    B. Romans
    C. Italians
    D. Germans

11. Which Spanish dish is based on rice, olive oil, and saffron cooked in one pot over an open flame?
    A. *Cocido*
    B. Paella
    C. *Fabada*
    D. *Picada*

12. Which group introduced Morocco to saffron, ginger, cumin, cinnamon, and the principles of combining sweet and sour flavors?
    A. Arabs
    B. Berbers
    C. Phoenicians
    D. Carthaginians

13. Which flavors describe the Moroccan cuisine?
    A. Spicy and pungent
    B. Sweet and savory
    C. Sweet, sour, and spicy
    D. Fresh, clean, and simple

14. The national dish of Morocco is
    A. paella.
    B. *harira.*
    C. *tagines.*
    D. couscous.

15. In Morocco, a thick stew of chickpeas, rice, meat (usually lamb), and vegetables, eaten with salad or bread, is known as
    A. *harira.*
    B. *tagines.*
    C. *B'stilla.*
    D. *bollito misto.*

16. What food is considered essential to Greece's well-being?
    A. Garlic
    B. Olives
    C. Peppers
    D. Tomatoes

17. A Greek casserole of lamb and eggplant, often covered with a layer of béchamel sauce or beaten egg before baking, is called
    A. baklava.
    B. moussaka.
    C. *shawarma.*
    D. *chakchouka.*

18. The two most important flavoring agents in Greek cuisine are
    A. olive oil and garlic.
    B. butter and canola oil.
    C. olive oil and lemon juice.
    D. clarified butter and lemon juice.

19. A Tunisian mixture of puréed onion and garlic combined with pungent spices such as chili and saffron is called
    A. *tabil.*
    B. *harissa.*
    C. *chermoula.*
    D. *chakchouka.*

20. The national dish of Egypt that is usually eaten at breakfast is
    A. *katteh.*
    B. *shawarma.*
    C. *ful medames.*
    D. *hamam mashi.*

21. In Egypt, shredded meat served in a pita with tahini is called
    A. *chermoula.*
    B. *shawarma.*
    C. *ful medames.*
    D. *hamam mashi.*

22. Which type of rice is made using the characteristic soak-boil-steam cooking technique, producing a light, fluffy grain?
    A. *Polo*
    B. *Damy*
    C. *Katteh*
    D. *Chelo*

23. An Iranian casserole of lamb cooked with walnut sauce and flavored with pomegranate is called
    A. biryani.
    B. *melohkia.*
    C. *shawarma.*
    D. *fesenjan.*

24. *Baharat* is a popular seasoning in which country?
    A. Iran
    B. Egypt
    C. Morocco
    D. Saudi Arabia

25. Which people were the first known to control the use of fire and apply it to cooking?
    A. Indian
    B. Chinese
    C. Japanese
    D. African

26. The Chinese belief that foods should not be forced to become something they are not, but should be kept in a natural, pure state, follows the philosophy of
    A. Taoism.
    B. Hinduism.
    C. Buddhism.
    D. Confucianism.

27. Which Chinese cuisine is known for its hot and spicy dishes?
    A. Canton
    B. Shandong
    C. Mandarin
    D. Szechwan Hunan

28. Which Chinese cuisine includes the dishes sweet and sour pork and egg foo yung?
    A. Canton
    B. Mandarin
    C. Shandong
    D. Szechwan Hunan

29. The Chinese cooking technique that is a long, slow braising in a mixture of soy sauce and water is called
    A. stewing.
    B. velveting.
    C. red cooking.
    D. flavor-potting.

30. In which country is drinking tea a very ancient and respected custom?
    A. India
    B. Japan
    C. Brazil
    D. Morocco

31. A Japanese food made from fermented soybean paste is called
    A. miso.
    B. *shoyu.*
    C. *dashi.*
    D. wasabi.

32. In India, which religion promotes vegetarianism?
    A. Judaism
    B. Jainism
    C. Hinduism
    D. Buddhism

33. An Indian spice mixture made from a variety of strong-tasting spices such as black cardamom, black pepper, and cloves is called

A. raan musallam.

B. garam masala.

C. panch phoron.

D. mangsho jhol.

34. The Indian cooking technique of scattering dry, whole, or ground spices into hot oil or ghee until they pop, flavoring the oil, is called

A. *dum.*

B. *tarka.*

C. *bhuna.*

D. *talana.*

35. A delicacy made by layering paper-thin sheets of pastry known as *warqa* with almonds and pastry cream is called

A. paella.

B. pastilla.

C. baklava.

D. moussaka.

36. A spice blend of black pepper, turmeric, ginger, cumin, and nutmeg used to season soups and stews is known as

A. *tabil.*

B. *harissa.*

C. *duqqa.*

D. *la kama.*

37. A popular Greek dip that consists of puréed chickpeas seasoned with lemon juice, olive oil, and sesame seed paste is called

A. salsa.

B. hummus.

C. taramosalata

D. avgolemono.

38. The Moroccan festival dish of steamed forequarter of lamb, flavored with cumin, is called

A. *choua.*

B. *harira.*

C. *b'stilla.*

D. *mechoui.*

39. The Neapolitan dish of cold veal with tuna sauce is called

A. *vitello tonnato.*

B. *bollito misto.*

C. pasta *con le sarde.*

D. *bistecca alla Fiorentina.*

40. A Tuscan specialty of grilled steak, at least 2 inches thick, is called

A. *saltimbocca.*

B. *bollito misto.*

C. pasta *con le sarde.*

D. *bistecca alla Fiorentina.*

Short Answer

1. _____ cuisine refers to the elaborate and delicate specialties prepared for the elite members of the imperial court in Peking.

2. Red cooking is a long, slow braising in a mixture of _____ and water.

3. The Japanese introduced cooking techniques such as baking and deep-frying, which were quickly adopted as _____.

4. In the Northern India cooking method called _____, the preparer covers the cooking pot, seals it with strips of dough, and then steams the food.

5. _____ are ground meat molded around a stick and grilled.

Essay

1. How do religious beliefs affect global cuisines? Give examples.

2. Determine what influences cuisines in different regions.

3. Generate a menu for a school lunch that you think would be acceptable to students and that includes foods from Greece. Compare them to foods we eat.

Final 1

True/False

_____ 1. Refrigerated dairy products should be stored at or below 41°F.

_____ 2. Butter and mayonnaise are common examples of condiments.

_____ 3. Vegans consume only grains, legumes, vegetables, fruit, nuts, and seeds.

_____ 4. Portion control means controlling the quantity of particular foods by using appropriately sized servings.

_____ 5. The as-purchased (AP) method is used to cost an ingredient at the purchase price before any trim or waste is taken into account.

_____ 6. Fixed costs remain the same regardless of sales volume.

_____ 7. Vinaigrette is the most stable and thickest emulsified dressing.

_____ 8. Intermezzo salads are large enough to serve as a full meal and also contain protein ingredients.

_____ 9. A production sheet lists all menu items that the chefs will prepare on a given day.

_____ 10. Nonperishable products are food products sold or distributed in a form that will spoil or decay within a limited period of time.

_____ 11. The tenderest cuts of meat come from those muscle groups that receive the least amount of exercise.

_____ 12. Cuts of meat with greater marbling or a thicker skin or fat cap produce juices that keep the meat moist while cooking, even in dry heat.

_____ 13. A press release is a brief presentation of promotional information written to sound like a news article.

_____ 14. Menu engineering systematically breaks down a menu's components to analyze which items are profitable and which items are not selling.

_____ 15. Soufflés are more stable than steamed puddings because of the greater percentage of eggs and sugar in their batter.

_____ 16. Gelato is an Italian version of ice cream that is made using most of the same ingredients as ice cream, but does not contain eggs.

_____ 17. All food waste can be composted.

_____ 18. Operations can reduce their amount of waste by reducing, reusing, and recycling.

_____ 19. *Curtido* is a traditional Central American relish that is made from cabbage, onions, and carrots tossed in vinegar.

_____ 20. *Sofrito* is a combination of aromatic ingredients that are quickly cooked together and then used as a foundation in soups and stews.

_____ 21. Grand cuisine is characterized by highly refined dishes and the creation of a strictly disciplined brigade system.

_____ 22. The flavors sweet, sour, and spicy describe Moroccan cuisine.

Multiple Choice

1. Fat is found in which part of the egg?
   A. Yolk
   B. Shell
   C. White
   D. Chalaza

2. The method used to cook eggs benedict and eggs Florentine is
   A. frying.
   B. baking.
   C. poaching.
   D. simmering.

3. On a ham and cheese sandwich with mustard, the ham and cheese are the
   A. spread.
   B. garnish.
   C. filling.
   D. condiment.

4. What type of sandwich is a club sandwich?
   A. Wrap
   B. Cold
   C. Submarine
   D. Multidecker

5. What is the cooking time for hard-boiled eggs?
   A. 10 minutes
   B. 15 minutes
   C. 20 minutes
   D. 25 minutes

6. Eggs that are fried only on the bottom are called
   A. up.
   B. basted.
   C. over easy.
   D. scrambled.

7. On a hamburger with ketchup, the ketchup is the
   A. garnish.
   B. spread.
   C. filling.
   D. condiment.

8. The body's energy is provided mainly by
   A. lipids.
   B. minerals.
   C. proteins.
   D. carbohydrates.

9. The chemical process that causes unsaturated fats to spoil is called
   A. absorption.
   B. digestion.
   C. oxidation.
   D. hydrogenation.

10. Chemical compounds found in food that are needed for regulating metabolic processes are called
    A. vitamins.
    B. proteins.
    C. fatty acids.
    D. amino acids

11. The condition in which the body cannot regulate blood sugar properly is called
    A. anemia.
    B. diabetes.
    C. anorexia.
    D. malnutrition.

12. The only source of energy for the brain and nervous system is
    A. fiber.
    B. sugar.
    C. insulin.
    D. glucose.

13. The minerals that help build strong bones and teeth are
    A. iron and zinc.
    B. sodium and calcium.
    C. potassium and sodium.
    D. calcium and phosphorous.

14. Vegans need to supplement their diet with which vitamin?
    A. A
    B. B
    C. C
    D. D

15. The condition that causes the bones to gradually lose their minerals and become weak and fragile is called
    A. diabetes.
    B. obesity.
    C. osteoporosis.
    D. cardiovascular disease.

16. The document that lists all menu items that are going to be prepared for a given date is called a
    A. receiving sheet.
    B. purchase order.
    C. master schedule.
    D. production sheet.

17. A compilation of sales and cost information for a specific period of time is presented in a(n)

    A. sales invoice.

    B. balance sheet.

    C. operating budget.

    D. profit-and-loss report.

18. Use the _____ method to minimize the value of the closing inventory.

    A. last in, first out (LIFO)

    B. actual purchase price

    C. latest purchase price

    D. weighted average purchase price

19. A vendor's document that lists such details as items purchased, date of order, purchaser, and sales price is called a(n)

    A. invoice.

    B. purchase order.

    C. receiving sheet.

    D. inventory record.

20. Which menu pricing method requires that an operation know the portion costs for each item sold?

    A. Average check

    B. Contribution margin

    C. Food cost percentage

    D. Straight markup pricing

21. The type of lettuce that is the essential ingredient in Caesar salad is

    A. bibb.

    B. leaf.

    C. iceberg.

    D. romaine.

22. The part of the salad that enhances appearance while also complementing overall taste is called the

    A. base.

    B. body.

    C. garnish.

    D. dressing.

23. A small portion of cole slaw is a type of _____ salad.

    A. main

    B. appetizer

    C. intermezzo

    D. accompaniment

24. How many days can unopened produce be stored?

    A. 2 to 3

    B. 4 to 5

    C. 6 to 7

    D. 8 to 9

25. An ingredient that can permanently bind unlike ingredients, such as oil and vinegar, is called a(n)

    A. solution.

    B. colloid.

    C. emulsifier.

    D. suspension.

26. The main ingredient in guacamole is

    A. potatoes.

    B. tomatoes.

    C. avocados.

    D. chickpeas.

27. What is the ingredient that holds a bound salad together?

    A. Milk

    B. Butter

    C. Olive oil

    D. Mayonnaise

28. The channel of distribution that includes the farmers and ranchers who raise produce and livestock is called the
    A. primary source.
    B. secondary source.
    C. tertiary source.
    D. intermediary source.

29. _____ is inspecting, accepting, and, in some cases, rejecting deliveries of goods and services.
    A. Storing
    B. Pilfering
    C. Receiving
    D. Ordering

30. What is the legally binding written document that details exactly what the buyer is ordering from the vendor called?
    A. Purchase order
    B. Inventory sheet
    C. Requisition form
    D. Production record

31. If a manager takes money or other goods from a person in exchange for purchasing from a specific vendor, this act is called a
    A. bribe.
    B. pilfer.
    C. payoff.
    D. kickback.

32. To forecast buying needs, buyers and managers use a(n)
    A. purchase order.
    B. inventory sheet.
    C. requisition form.
    D. production record.

33. The ideal amount of inventory items that an operation should have at all times is called
    A. par stock.
    B. par value.
    C. perpetual inventory.
    D. periodic inventory.

34. What is the highest quality USDA grade of beef?
    A. Good
    B. Select
    C. Prime
    D. Choice

35. Italian salami and pepperoni are examples of _____ sausage.
    A. fresh
    B. cured
    C. dried
    D. smoked

36. What color are the juices when poultry is done cooking?
    A. Red
    B. Pink
    C. Clear
    D. Brown

37. Shellfish identification tags must be kept on file for _____ days from the date the last shellfish was sold or served.
    A. 30
    B. 60
    C. 90
    D. 120

38. The process of removing a shrimp's digestive tract is called
    A. deveining.
    B. trimming.
    C. trussing.
    D. shucking.

39. Small, round pieces of meat that are molded by wrapping them in cheesecloth are called
    A. scallops.
    B. noisettes.
    C. medallions.
    D. tenderloin.

40. The connective tissue that attaches the meat to the bone and will not break down during cooking is called
    A. collagen.
    B. fibrous.
    C. adipose.
    D. elastin.

41. Which element of the contemporary marketing mix is a way in which an operation tells its customers about its products and services?
    A. Presentation mix
    B. Communication mix
    C. Product-service mix
    D. Contemporary marketing mix

42. The list of action steps necessary for an operation to sell a product or service is called a
    A. marketing plan.
    B. promotion mix.
    C. research report.
    D. mission statement.

43. The market research method that tries out a product for a limited time or with a limited group of people is
    A. surveying.
    B. sampling.
    C. observational.
    D. experimental.

44. The type of segmentation that breaks down a large market into smaller groups of similar individuals is called
    A. lifestyle.
    B. market.
    C. benefit.
    D. demographic.

45. The type of menu that prices each item separately is called
    A. du jour.
    B. limited.
    C. cyclical.
    D. á la carte.

46. The menu item classification that has a high menu mix percentage and a low contribution margin is
    A. dog.
    B. star.
    C. puzzle.
    D. plowhorse.

47. Which menu, similar to a prix fixe menu, bundles various elements into one package?
    A. Fixed
    B. Cyclical
    C. California
    D. Table d'hôte

48. The baking ingredient that determines the consistency of the finished product is
    A. sweetener.
    B. thickener.
    C. leavening.
    D. shortening.

49. Which type of dough is made by adding shortening or tenderizing ingredients such as sugar, syrup, butter, eggs, milk, and cream?
    A. Soft
    B. Rich
    C. Sour
    D. Sponge

50. Which method is used to prepare cakes with the lightest texture, such as angel food and chiffon cakes?
    A. Foaming
    B. Creaming
    C. Two-stage
    D. Straight mix

51. The ingredient that makes baked goods moist, adds flavor, and keeps them fresh is called
    A. gluten.
    B. shortening.
    C. leavening.
    D. thickener.

52. What type of dough is used to make French bread?
    A. Soft
    B. Lean
    C. Sponge
    D. Sourdough

53. What is the term used to describe the white coating that sometimes appears on the surface of chocolate?
    A. Nibs
    B. Mold
    C. Bloom
    D. Crystal

54. A sauce made from fresh berries or other fruits is called
    A. bloom.
    B. syrup.
    C. extract.
    D. coulis.

55. The type of renewable energy source that converts energy to electricity using photovoltaics is
    A. wind.
    B. solar.
    C. biomass.
    D. geothermal.

56. Meeting current resource needs without compromising the ability to accommodate future needs is called what?
    A. Preservation
    B. Conservation
    C. Sustainability
    D. Compromising

57. What percentage of the United States relies on groundwater to supply its households and businesses with water?
    A. 30
    B. 40
    C. 50
    D. 60

58. Which area in a restaurant or foodservice operation uses the most energy?
    A. Lighting
    B. Refrigeration
    C. Heating/cooling
    D. Cooking equipment

59. Which color of recycling bin is used for glass and plastics?
    A. Blue
    B. Green
    C. Black
    D. Yellow

60. The type of system on an aquaculture farm that reconditions and reuses water is called
    A. open.
    B. closed.
    C. controlled.
    D. uncontrolled.

61. Which region is home to fusion cuisine?
    A. South
    B. Northwest
    C. Southwest
    D. Pacific Rim

62. In Jamaica, what is rubbed on meat to make it spicy?
    A. Allspice
    B. Creole rub
    C. Jerk spice
    D. Horseradish

63. Which flavors describe the foods of Central America?
    A. Sweet and sour
    B. Mild and earthy
    C. Salty and heavy
    D. Light and nutritious

64. What ingredients are in the trinity of Cajun and Creole cuisine?
    A. Carrots, onions, and celery
    B. Celery, onions, and tomatoes
    C. Celery, onions, and green bell peppers
    D. Scallions, tomatoes, and sweet potatoes

65. The spicy Cajun rice dish made up of chicken, andouille sausage, shrimp, crayfish, trinity, other vegetables, herbs, broth, and seasonings is known as
    A. gumbo.
    B. ceviche.
    C. andouille.
    D. jambalaya.

66. The style of cooking that originated in the swamps and bayous of southwestern Louisiana is called
    A. Creole.
    B. Cajun.
    C. tidewater.
    D. low country.

67. The Scandinavians introduced the Midwest to
    A. lefse.
    B. pasties.
    C. goulash.
    D. sauerkraut.

68. Which European country is credited with creating the mother sauces?
A. Italy
B. Spain
C. France
D. Belgium

69. Who introduced Spain to citrus fruits, almonds, sugarcane, rice, saffron, and a wide variety of vegetables and spices?
A. Arabs
B. Romans
C. Italians
D. Iroquois

70. What is the national soup of Morocco?
A. Paella
B. *Harira*
C. Couscous
D. Gazpacho

71. The type of Middle Eastern cookery that uses the characteristic soak-boil-steam technique to produce a light, fluffy rice is
A. *polow.*
B. *damy.*
C. *kateh.*
D. *chelow.*

72. The first known people to control the use of fire and apply it to the cooking of food were the
A. Arabs.
B. Indians.
C. Chinese.
D. Japanese.

73. The Chinese belief that foods should not be forced to become something they are not, but should be kept in their most natural and pure state, follows the philosophy of
A. Taoism
B. Hinduism.
C. Buddhism.
D. Confucianism.

Short Answer:

1. Milk that has been heated to destroy harmful bacteria has been _____.

2. An egg is composed of the outer shell, the white (albumen), and the _____.

3. _____ is putting eggs into cold water immediately after cooking to stop the cooking and make them easier to peel.

4. Energy from food is measured in units called _____.

5. Chemicals that kill insects and other plant pests are called _____.

6. _____ is essential for replenishing red blood cells.

7. With the _____ method, total revenue is divided by the number of seats, average seat turnover, and days open in a year.

8. A(n) _____ is a chart that shows employees' names and the days and times they are to work.

9. _____ is the price an operation pays out for the purchasing and preparation of its products or in providing its services.

10. _____ salads are usually sweet and often contain fruits, sweetened gelatin, nuts, cream, and whipped cream.

11. _____ dressing in its simplest form is made of oil and vinegar.

12. _____ is the most stable and thickest emulsified dressing.

13. _____ are specialized, written price lists created for an operation by a supplier.

14. A(n) _____ sheet lists all menu items that the chefs will prepare on a given day.

15. _____ levels are the ideal amounts of inventory items that an operation should have at all times.

16. _____ measures the proportion of edible or usable meat after it has been trimmed of bones or fat.

17. _____is a mixture of lean ground meat and fat that is emulsified, or forced together, in a food grinder and then pushed through a sieve to create a very smooth paste.

18. _____ meat is organ meat from hogs, cattle, or sheep.

19. _____ involve interacting with the people in the local area to create awareness of and trust for an operation.

20. A(n) _____ is an analysis of the popularity and profitability of a group of menu items.

21. A(n) _____ menu lists all meals available at any time of day.

22. When a product containing refined sugars is baked, the heat causes the sugar to turn a light brown in a process called _____.

23. Flavorful oils taken from such foods as vanilla, lemon, and almond are called _____.

24. In baking, ingredients are given percentages in relation to _____.

25. A(n) _____ building is one that has been designed, built, renovated, or reused so that the structure conserves energy, uses resources more efficiently, and reduces the overall impact on the environment.

26. _____ is food that customers did not eat, but that back-of-the-house staff prepared, cooked, cooled, and held safely.

27. A(n) _____ source offers food produced in the surrounding growing region.

28. _____ is a hearty soup often made with trinity, shrimp, and okra, and thickened with brown roux and filé.

29. Barbecue originated in the _____.

30. _____ is a tropical tree that produces seed pods containing the beans that are ground to make cocoa powder, which is then made into chocolate.

31. The signature cooking methods in Morocco are *couscoussière* and _____.

32. The Chinese cuisine that is known for its hot and spicy foods is _____.

33. _____ is made by the characteristic soak-boil-steam technique, producing a light, fluffy rice.

Essay

1. The USDA offers voluntary grading of meat. What are the two grades that they assign to most types of meat and what does each measure?

2. What are the two types of yeast bread dough and what differentiates them?

3. Both Italy and Morocco border the Mediterranean, yet they have very different cuisines. Describe the difference in traditional flavors between Italian dishes and Moroccan dishes and provide examples of common cooking methods in each country.

4. Pricing food is a very complicated process. Food costs must be controlled during all stages of the food flow process. Describe the steps of this process and how food costs may be controlled at each step.

5. Identify the two types of vitamins and explain how they differ.

Final 2

True/False

_____ 1. Soufflés are made with whipped egg yolks.

_____ 2. Cheddar and gruyère are examples of firm-ripened cheeses.

_____ 3. Osteoporosis is a condition in which the bones gradually lose their minerals and become weak and fragile.

_____ 4. Soluble fiber dissolves in water.

_____ 5. A recipe cost card is a tool used to calculate the standard portion cost for a menu item.

_____ 6. Fixed costs, in contrast to variable costs, change based on the operation's sales.

_____ 7. Vinaigrettes are lighter, thinner dressings often used on more delicate ingredients.

_____ 8. An emulsion is a temporary mixture of ingredients that eventually separates back into its unique parts.

_____ 9. The official procedure that employees use when taking an item out of the storeroom and putting it into production is called issuing.

_____ 10. A written invoice should accompany every delivery.

_____ 11. Game meat is meat from animals that have been raised domestically.

_____ 12. Dark meat is higher in calories and fat.

_____ 13. Demographics refer to the ways in which researchers categorize or group people, which can be done in a number of ways.

_____ 14. The contribution margin is defined as the amount of money remaining for an operation after expenses, or costs, are paid.

_____ 15. Quick breads and cakes use the same mixing methods.

_____ 16. 3-2-1 dough is made of 3 parts flour, 2 parts fat, and 1 part water.

_____ 17. Almost 75 percent of the Earth's surface is covered with water, but only 5 percent of that can be used by humans, either as groundwater or as freshwater.

_____ 18. A brownfield site is an abandoned, polluted industrial site that can be cleaned up and repurposed for commercial use.

_____ 19. Comals are clay pots used in Mexican cooking.

_____ 20. Peppers are a major flavoring agent of Mexican food in all regions.

_____ 21. *Baharat* is a popular seasoning in Saudi Arabia.

_____ 22. The Chinese belief that foods should not be forced to become something they are not, but should be kept in their most natural and pure state, follows the philosophy of Tao.

Multiple Choice

1. Eggs cooked for immediate service should reach an internal temperature of _____ for 15 seconds.
   A. 145°F
   B. 155°F
   C. 165°F
   D. 175°F

2. The part of an egg that also is known as the albumen is the
   A. yolk.
   B. white.
   C. shell.
   D. chalaza.

3. Which type of cheese has mold injected or sprayed into the cheese to spread throughout it while it ages?
   A. Firm, ripened
   B. Soft-ripened
   C. Blue-veined
   D. Unripened, fresh

4. The process in which dairies make cheese by separating the milk's solids from its liquid is called
   A. curdling.
   B. clarification.
   C. pasteurization.
   D. homogenization.

5. In which cooking method are eggs constantly stirred?
   A. Baking
   B. Frying
   C. Shirring
   D. Scrambling

6. A savory egg custard baked in a crust is called a(n)
   A. frittata.
   B. omelet.
   C. soufflé.
   D. quiche.

7. Which type of sandwich consists of 2 slices of bread or 2 halves of a roll, a spread, and a filling?
   A. Cold
   B. Wrap
   C. Grilled
   D. Submarine

8. Which process alters the physical properties of fats and makes them stay fresh longer?
   A. Digestion
   B. Evaporation
   C. Absorption
   D. Hydrogenation

9. Olive, canola, and peanut oil are sources of which type of fat?
   A. Saturated
   B. Cholesterol
   C. Monounsaturated
   D. Polyunsaturated

10. The nutrients needed to build new cells and repair injured ones are
    A. lipids.
    B. minerals.
    C. vitamins.
    D. proteins.

11. Meat, poultry, and fish are examples of which type of protein?
    A. Complete
    B. Incomplete
    C. Complementary
    D. Noncomplementary

12. The condition that occurs when the body does not get enough nutrients is called
    A. anemia.
    B. anorexia.
    C. malnutrition.
    D. osteoporosis.

13. Which 2 nutrients are lost when meat is cooked too long?
    A. Iron and potassium
    B. Vitamin A and iron
    C. Protein and vitamin B12
    D. Thiamine and vitamin B6

14. The substance found in food that promotes digestive health and regularity is called
    A. fiber.
    B. starch.
    C. fatty acids.
    D. cholesterol.

15. Which type of vegetarian consumes vegetarian items plus dairy products?
    A. Vegan
    B. Ovo
    C. Lacto
    D. Lacto-ovo

16. A record of the number of portions of every item sold on a menu is called a
    A. sales history.
    B. sales invoice.
    C. receiving sheet.
    D. production sheet.

17. Income from the sale of food items is called
    A. revenue.
    B. expenses.
    C. fixed cost.
    D. gross profit.

18. When is the cost of a food item incurred?
    A. When it is ordered.
    B. When it is consumed.
    C. When it is budgeted.
    D. When it is purchased.

19. Which classification of cost covers a lease and utilities?
    A. Non-fixed
    B. Variable
    C. Controllable
    D. Uncontrollable

20. The inventory method that assumes that stock has been rotated during the month is called
    A. first in, first out (FIFO).
    B. last in, first out (LIFO).
    C. latest purchase price.
    D. weighted average purchase price.

21. The most popular American salad green is
    A. endive.
    B. arugula.
    C. iceberg lettuce.
    D. romaine lettuce.

22. The part of the salad that is made up of a layer of greens that line the plate or bowl in which the salad is served is called the
    A. base.
    B. body.
    C. garnish.
    D. dressing.

23. The salad type that stimulates the appetite and is light enough for the first course is the
    A. appetizer.
    B. intermezzo.
    C. main course.
    D. accompaniment.

24. At which temperature range should loose salad greens be stored?
    A. 29°F to 35°F
    B. 36°F to 41°F
    C. 42°F to 47°F
    D. 48°F to 55°F

25. The standard recipe for a basic vinaigrette is
    A. 1 part oil, 1 part vinegar.
    B. 2 parts oil, 2 parts vinegar.
    C. 3 parts oil, 2 parts vinegar.
    D. 3 parts oil, 1 part vinegar.

26. Grilled chicken Caesar salad is a type of _____ salad.
    A. starter
    B. main course
    C. intermezzo
    D. accompaniment

27. What enhances the appearance of a salad, while also complementing the overall taste?
    A. Dip
    B. Filling
    C. Garnish
    D. Vinaigrette

28. A buyer must place an order for crushed tomatoes. Par stock is 15 cases, 8 cases are in stock, and 3 cases will be used before delivery. How many cases should the buyer order?
    A. 8
    B. 9
    C. 10
    D. 11

29. In which channel of distribution does the company buy food items from a farmer and then resell those same food items to a retailer?
    A. Distiller
    B. Manufacturer
    C. Primary source
    D. Intermediary source

30. The purchasing method that includes verbal price quotes is called
    A. time value.
    B. basic purchasing.
    C. formal purchasing.
    D. informal purchasing.

31. The purchasing form that describes in detail the characteristics of products and services that an operation wants to buy is called a(n)
    A. requisition form.
    B. purchase order.
    C. inventory sheet.
    D. specifications form.

32. To purchase a new piece of kitchen equipment, a chef must fill out a
    A. receiving sheet.
    B. purchase order.
    C. requisition form.
    D. product specification.

33. The process of inspecting, accepting, or rejecting deliveries of goods and services is called
    A. issuing.
    B. storing.
    C. pilfering.
    D. receiving.

34. What is the tough membrane on meat called?
    A. Tenderloin
    B. Silverskin
    C. Noisettes
    D. Medallions

35. A fish that has had its viscera, scales, fins, and often its head removed is a _____fish.
    A. drawn
    B. steak
    C. whole
    D. dressed

36. The category of shellfish that includes those with a single internal shell and tentacles is called
    A. finfish.
    B. mollusks.
    C. crustaceans.
    D. cephalopods.

37. Flounder and halibut are examples of
    A. flatfish.
    B. roundfish.
    C. crustaceans.
    D. cephalopods.

38. The best cooking method for tougher cuts of meat is
    A. frying.
    B. grilling.
    C. braising.
    D. sautéing.

39. The fabrication technique in which a piece of meat is cut lengthwise nearly in half, so that it opens out and lies flat, is called
    A. trimming.
    B. filleting.
    C. trussing.
    D. butterflying.

40. Which grade of seafood is marked with a stamp?
    A. A
    B. B
    C. C
    D. D

41. A collection of people with similar, specific needs and wants is called a
    A. club.
    B. group.
    C. market.
    D. segment.

42. What is the process of communicating a business's messages to its market called?
    A. Marketing
    B. Presenting
    C. Servicing
    D. Positioning

43. Which element of the contemporary marketing mix includes all the food and services offered by an operation to a customer?
    A. Presentation
    B. Communication
    C. Product-service
    D. Place-promotion

44. The market research method that gathers information through telephone, e-mail, or tableside is
    A. sampling.
    B. surveying.
    C. observational.
    D. experimental.

45. The type of marketing that treats people as different from each other and tries to make a focused appeal to a distinct group of customers is called _____ marketing.
    A. mass
    B. target
    C. demographic
    D. geographic

46. The type of market segmentation that analyzes the heavy users of a product or service is
    A. lifestyle.
    B. benefit.
    C. product usage.
    D. unique selling.

47. The type of menu that lists the menu items available on a particular day is
A. du jour.
B. fixed.
C. limited.
D. cyclical.

48. The ingredient that provides moisture to a baked product and allows the gluten to develop properly is
A. yeast.
B. extract.
C. butter.
D. liquid.

49. Which type of cookie includes peanut butter cookies?
A. Bar
B. Sheet
C. Rolled
D. Molded

50. Which method for preparing quick breads and cake batters is used to prepare products with a more refined crumb and dense, rich texture?
A. Creaming
B. 2-stage
C. Foaming
D. Straight mix

51. What is the process called when a baker allows yeast dough to rise just before baking?
A. Proofing
B. Yeasting
C. Kneading
D. Portioning

52. Which type of dough is used to make pie crust?
A. 3-2-1
B. Soft
C. Lean
D. Phyllo

53. This is an elegant, rich, many-layered cake often filled with buttercream or jam.
A. Torte
B. Coulis
C. Baklava
D. Sabayon

54. If chocolate becomes grainy or scorched during tempering, the baker should
A. add more liquid.
B. reheat the chocolate.
C. reduce the heat.
D. discard the chocolate.

55. The renewable energy source that contains stored energy from the sun amassed through photosynthesis is
A. wind.
B. solar.
C. biomass.
D. geothermal.

56. What is the practice of limiting the use of a resource called?
A. Preservation
B. Conservation
C. Sustainability
D. Reduction

57. Each day, the United States uses approximately how many millions of gallons of fresh water?
    A. 240
    B. 350
    C. 450
    D. 550

58. The type of environment in which food has been within the kitchen's control and has been kept safe from cross-contamination and time-temperature abuse is called
    A. open.
    B. closed.
    C. controlled.
    D. uncontrolled.

59. What temperature should water be for handwashing?
    A. 100°F
    B. 110°F
    C. 120°F
    D. 130°F

60. Using a resource today in ways that don't hurt the future ability to use that same resource is called
    A. preservation.
    B. conservation.
    C. sustainability.
    D. reduction.

61. In the Southwestern cuisine Tex-Mex, the meats are
    A. diced.
    B. minced.
    C. ground.
    D. shredded.

62. What is the flavor profile of the cuisine of the Southwestern United States?
    A. Sweet and sour
    B. Salty and savory
    C. Hot and earthy
    D. Smoky and spicy

63. What style of cooking and presenting food combines the ingredients and techniques of Asian and West Coast cuisine?
    A. Haute
    B. Fusion
    C. Classical
    D. Barbecue

64. The cuisine that began by blending French grand cuisine principles with the cooking techniques of enslaved Africans is called
    A. Creole.
    B. Cajun.
    C. tidewater.
    D. low country.

65. The Central American dish that is a mix of white rice and black beans, cooked separately and then fried together in coconut oil, is called
    A. *sofrito.*
    B. *curtido.*
    C. andouille.
    D. *gallo pinto.*

66. Which Peruvian signature dish mixes key lime citrus juice with raw fish?
    A. Ceviche
    B. Sashimi
    C. *Feijoada*
    D. *Papa rellena*

67. The staples of Bolivia are potatoes, rice, beans, and
  A. yucca.
  B. quinoa.
  C. scallions.
  D. bananas.

68. What are the major cooking fats of Italy?
  A. Olive oil and butter
  B. Butter and canola oil
  C. Margarine and egg yolks
  D. Clarified butter and vegetable oil

69. The group of people who introduced the Moroccans to saffron, ginger, cumin, cinnamon, and the principles of combining sweet and sour flavors were the
  A. Arabs.
  B. Berbers.
  C. Romans.
  D. Carthaginians.

70. What are the most important flavoring agents in Greek cuisine?
  A. Olive oil and butter
  B. Garlic and olive oil
  C. Garlic and lemon juice
  D. Olive oil and lemon juice

71. What Chinese cooking technique is a long, slow braising in a mixture of soy sauce and water?
  A. Stewing
  B. Velveting
  C. Red cooking
  D. Flavor-potting

72. What is the Neapolitan dish of cold veal with tuna sauce called?
  A. *Vitello tonnato*
  B. *Bollito misto*
  C. Pasta *con le sarde*
  D. *Bistecca alla Fiorentina*

73. The Chinese cuisine that includes the dishes sweet and sour pork and egg foo yung is
  A. Canton.
  B. Shandong.
  C. Mandarin.
  D. Szechwan Hunan.

Short Answer:

1. _____ eggs are cracked open and combined in a container.

2. _____ is a hot, open-faced Italian pie with a crisp, yeast dough bottom.

3. _____ sandwiches are small, cold sandwiches usually served on bread or toast, trimmed of their crusts, and cut into shapes.

4. Chemicals that aid the body in fighting or preventing diseases are called
    _____.

5. Products that have been produced without pesticides or synthetic fertilizers are called
    _____.

6. The recommended daily nutrient and energy intake amounts for healthy people of a
    particular age range and gender are called _____.

7. _____ is the portion of dollars that a particular menu item
    contributes to overall profits.

8. A(n) _____ is a prediction of sales levels or costs that will occur
    during a specific time period.

9. _____ represents the dollar value of a food product in storage and
    can be expressed in terms of units, values, or both.

10. The _____ salad is intended to be a palate cleanser after a rich
    dinner and before dessert.

11. If a restaurant or foodservice operation runs out of food, it is called a(n)
    _____.

12. A(n) _____ is a legally binding written document that details
    exactly what the buyer is ordering from the vendor.

13. A(n) _____ is a written record that ensures the vendor will credit
    the operation for a rejected item.

14. The _____ of the operation is the amount of funds available to it at
    any given time.

15. _____ refers to the amount of water moisture in the air or in a
    contained space such as a refrigerator.

16. Butchers hang the meat during _____ to help lengthen the muscle
    fibers and increase the tenderness of the meat.

17. _____ have a backbone and can live in fresh water or in the ocean.

18. _____ is the opening or removing of a mollusk's shell.

19. The process of communicating a business's message to its market is called
    _____.

20. _____ marketing treats everyone as having the same needs and
    wants.

21. _____ refer to how researchers categorize or group people, which can be done in a number of ways.

22. _____ is the procedure for preparing a pre-baked pie shell.

23. The process of melting chocolate is called _____.

24. If the dessert sauce crème anglaise begins to overheat, it can _____, or develop lumps.

25. Fuels that are formed from plant or animal remains buried deep in the earth are called _____.

26. _____ do not rely on a finite supply of a resource, directly emit greenhouse gases, or contribute to air pollution.

27. _____ is a natural form of recycling that occurs when organic material decomposes to form organic fertilizer.

28. In Cal-Mex, meats are _____.

29. _____ means sauce or mixture, and can sometimes be used as a suffix on words to describe the sauce.

30. A(n) _____ looks like a fat, homemade tortilla, but is actually a pan-fried corn biscuit filled with cheese, beans, pork, or chicken.

31. An important cooking method in northern India is _____, in which the preparer covers the cooking pot, seals it with strips of dough, and steams the food.

32. Chinese cuisine is based on the yin and yang philosophy of the _____.

33. The flour that is most frequently used in Italian cuisine is _____.

Essay

1. What are the differences in the fat content of buttermilk, evaporated milk, and condensed milk, and how are each of these made?

2. Identify and describe 4 basic parts of a salad and the appropriate ingredients to use for each part.

3. Name and describe the 3 primary elements of the contemporary marketing mix.

4. Identify 3 ways in which the restaurant and foodservice industry can help to save water, while still protecting food and meeting the needs of customers?

5. Compare the flavor profiles of the different parts of the United States—the Northeast, the Midwest, the South, the Southwest, and the Pacific Coast/Rim.

Chapter 1
Breakfast Foods and Sandwiches

True/False

1. ANS: T
REF: 10

2. ANS: T
REF: 12

3. ANS: T
REF: 53

4. ANS: F
REF: 46

5. ANS: F
REF: 16

Multiple Choice

1. ANS: C
REF: 6

2. ANS: B
REF: 12

3. ANS: D
REF: 12

4. ANS: A
REF: 14

5. ANS: D
REF: 16

6. ANS: A
REF: 16

7. ANS: C
REF: 17

8. ANS: C
REF: 17

9. ANS: C
REF: 17

10. ANS: B
REF: 19

11. ANS: C
REF: 20

12. ANS: D
REF: 25

13. ANS: C
    REF: 25

14. ANS: B
    REF: 25

15. ANS: C
    REF: 28

16. ANS: D
    REF: 18

17. ANS: B
    REF: 25

18. ANS: A
    REF: 40

19. ANS: D
    REF: 41

20. ANS: A
    REF: 43

21. ANS: C
    REF: 46

22. ANS: B
    REF: 46

23. ANS: D
    REF: 55

24. ANS: C
    REF: 54

25. ANS: A
    REF: 54

26. ANS: A
    REF: 57

27. ANS: B
    REF: 57

28. ANS: D
    REF: 58

29. ANS: B
    REF: 57

30. ANS: C
    REF: 62

31. ANS: B
    REF: 55

32. ANS: C
    REF: 64

33. ANS: C
    REF: 54

34. ANS: C
    REF: 56

35. ANS: B
    REF: 47

36. ANS: C
    REF: 25

37. ANS: B
    REF: 16

38. ANS: A
    REF: 17

39. ANS: B
    REF: 42

40. ANS: A
    REF: 25

Short Answer

1. ANS: smoke point
   REF: 12

2. ANS: Basted
   REF: 25

3. ANS: Herbal
   REF: 46

4. ANS: Pizza
   REF: 54

5. ANS: Tea
   REF: 56

Essay

1. ANS: To be acceptable, shell eggs must also meet the following criteria:
   - No odor
   - Clean and unbroken shells
   - Reject any shell eggs with an off odor, a sulfur smell, or dirty or cracked shells.

When delivered, refrigerate liquid and frozen eggs at or below 45°F unless the eggs should stay frozen.

Store fresh eggs immediately in refrigeration at an air temperature of 45°F or lower.

Store liquid eggs according to the manufacturer's recommendations.

Place dried egg products in a cool, dry storeroom. Once egg product has been mixed with water, store at 41°F or lower.

No matter how they are prepared, always follow safety steps to ensure properly cooked eggs:
   - Handle pooled eggs carefully. Pooled eggs are eggs that are cracked open and combined in a container. Cook them immediately after mixing, or store them at 41°F or lower.
   - Wash and sanitize the containers used to hold pooled eggs before making a new batch.
   - Keep shell eggs in cold storage until ready for use. Take out only as many eggs as needed for immediate use.

REF: 22

2. ANS: Bacon is about 70 percent fat and shrinks quite a bit. Canadian bacon is similar to ham and is much leaner than regular bacon.

REF: 41

3. ANS: In the broadest sense of the word, sandwiches may be served in a variety of ways—open-faced on one slice of bread, rolled up in a piece of bread (such as a wrap sandwich), or even on a flat crust (such as pizza). While not a typical sandwich, pizza is hot, open-faced, and has a tremendous variety of toppings or fillings and sauces as well. Examples include chicken alfredo, Hawaiian with pineapple and Canadian bacon, and taco pizza.

REF: 53

Chapter 2
Nutrition

True/False

1. ANS: T
REF: 94

2. ANS: T
REF: 86

3. ANS: F
REF: 93

4. ANS: F
REF: 96

5. ANS: F
REF: 112

Multiple Choice

1. ANS: A
REF: 80

2. ANS: B
REF: 87

3. ANS: D
REF: 84

4. ANS: B
REF: 87

5. ANS: B
REF: 90

6. ANS: D
REF: 90

7. ANS: A
REF: 91

8. ANS: B
REF: 92

9. ANS: C
REF: 93

10. ANS: B
REF: 94

11. ANS: D
REF: 95

12. ANS: B
REF: 95

13. ANS: C
REF: 96

14. ANS: B
REF: 98

15. ANS: D
    REF: 100

16. ANS: D
    REF: 100

17. ANS: D
    REF: 27

18. ANS: C
    REF: 101

19. ANS: C
    REF: 111

20. ANS: C
    REF: 126

21. ANS: C
    REF: 113

22. ANS: D
    REF: 92

23. ANS: A
    REF: 85

24. ANS: B
    REF: 88

25. ANS: D
    REF: 85

26. ANS: C
    REF: 87

27. ANS: C
    REF: 87

28. ANS: B
    REF: 90

29. ANS: D
    REF: 91

30. ANS: D
    REF: 92

31. ANS: B
    REF: 92

32. ANS: D
    REF: 95

33. ANS: A
    REF: 93

34. ANS: A
    REF: 100

35. ANS: B
    REF: 100

36. ANS: B
    REF: 101

37. ANS: C
    REF: 106

38. ANS: C
    REF: 103

39. ANS: B
    REF: 127

40. ANS: D
    REF: 84

Short Answer

1. ANS: Simple
   REF: 86

2. ANS: Insoluble
   REF: 88

3. ANS: Cholesterol
   REF: 90

4. ANS: water
   REF: 94

5. ANS: genetically modified organisms
   REF: 126

Essay

1. ANS: Water is essential for the digestion, absorption, and transportation of nutrients and for the elimination of waste through the kidneys, colon, and lungs. The human body can live a long time without many other nutrients, but only a few days without water. Other sources of water include juices, fruits, and vegetables.
   REF: 96

2. ANS: Vitamins are chemical mixtures found in foods that help carbohydrates, proteins, fats, and minerals work properly. Water-soluable vitamins (vitamins C and B) mix only with water. Fat-soluble vitamins (vitamins A, D, E, and K) mix only with fat. They are needed for regulating metabolic processes, such as digestion and the absorption of nutrients. They are essential for life.
   REF: 94

3. ANS: Wash vegetables quickly and thoroughly, never soak vegetables, avoid excessive trimming, and prepare vegetables and fruit as close to serving time as possible.
   REF: 114

Chapter 3
Cost Control

True/False

1. ANS: T
REF: 203

2. ANS: T
REF: 202

3. ANS: F
REF: 147

4. ANS: T
REF: 167

5. ANS: F
REF: 177

Multiple Choice

1. ANS: C
REF: 148

2. ANS: D
REF: 148

3. ANS: C
REF: 151

4. ANS: B
REF: 152

5. ANS: A
REF: 153

6. ANS: D
REF: 153

7. ANS: A
REF: 178

8. ANS: C
REF: 156

9. ANS: C
REF: 156

10. ANS: A
REF: 157

11. ANS: D
REF: 157

12. ANS: A
REF: 167

13. ANS: B
REF: 168

14. ANS: B
REF: 168

15. ANS: D
    REF: 176

16. ANS: C
    REF: 178

17. ANS: B
    REF: 178

18. ANS: C
    REF: 179

19. ANS: B
    REF: 168

20. ANS: A
    REF: 169–170

21. ANS: C
    REF: 178

22. ANS: D
    REF: 189

23. ANS: A
    REF: 191

24. ANS: C
    REF: 199

25. ANS: B
    REF: 200

26. ANS: B
    REF: 200

27. ANS: A
    REF: 201

28. ANS: A
    REF: 202

29. ANS: D
    REF: 205

30. ANS: D
    REF: 167

31. ANS: A
    REF: 205

32. ANS: C
    REF: 187

33. ANS: D
    REF: 148

34. ANS: D
    REF: 167

35. ANS: A
    REF: 177

36. ANS: C
    REF: 205

37. ANS: C
    REF: 152

38. ANS: B
    REF: 167

39. ANS: A
    REF: 185

40. ANS: B
    REF: 147

Short Answer

1. ANS: point-of-sale (POS) systems
   REF: 153

2. ANS: Full-line supplier
   REF: 158

3. ANS: Inventory
   REF: 167

4. ANS: as-purchased
   REF: 170

5. ANS: contribution margin
   REF: 178

Essay

1. ANS: The menu determines the number of employees needed at any given time. Labor costs are controlled by forecasting how many customers can be expected for meal times and how many employees are needed to meet foodservice schedules. When more preparation time is needed to produce food items, labor costs will be higher.
   REF: 187–189

2. ANS: In order to control menu costs, managers must forecast sales of menu items. Forecasting uses data to predict what is likely to happen in the future. Forecasting is a successful tool for menu planning.
   REF: 155–156

3. ANS: Improper purchasing, inaccurate forecasting, poor receiving procedures, failure to follow standardized recipes, poor production schedules, lack of good selling and service, and improper selection of menu items can all contribute to high food costs.
   REF: 165–166

Chapter 4
Salads and Garnishing

True/False

1. ANS: T
REF: 248

2. ANS: T
REF: 252

3. ANS: F
REF: 254

4. ANS: F
REF: 225

5. ANS: T
REF: 221

Multiple Choice

1. ANS: C
REF: 220

2. ANS: D
REF: 220

3. ANS: D
REF: 220

4. ANS: A
REF: 221

5. ANS: C
REF: 222

6. ANS: B
REF: 223

7. ANS: D
REF: 226

8. ANS: A
REF: 235

9. ANS: D
REF: 235

10. ANS: C
REF: 235

11. ANS: B
REF: 237

12. ANS: A
REF: 238

13. ANS: A
REF: 225

14. ANS: D
REF: 232

15. ANS: C
REF: 244

16. ANS: C
REF: 245

17. ANS: B
REF: 245

18. ANS: B
REF: 245

19. ANS: D
REF: 245

20. ANS: C
REF: 247

21. ANS: B
REF: 248

22. ANS: D
REF: 252

23. ANS: C
REF: 252

24. ANS: C
REF: 245

25. ANS: D
REF: 260

26. ANS: A
REF: 264

27. ANS: C
REF: 267

28. ANS: D
REF: 268

29. ANS: C
REF: 267

30. ANS: C
REF: 267

31. ANS: C
REF: 267

32. ANS: C
REF: 237

33. ANS: D
REF: 225

34. ANS: C
REF: 233

35. ANS: B
REF: 268

36. ANS: A
REF: 225

37. ANS: B
REF: 225

38. ANS: B
REF: 235

39. ANS: D
REF: 235

40. ANS: A
REF: 235

Short Answer

1. ANS: Garnish
   REF: 222

2. ANS: composed
   REF: 225

3. ANS: suspension
   REF: 244

4. ANS: Emulsified vinaigrette
   REF: 245

5. ANS: Dips
   REF: 251

Essay

1. ANS: A salad dressing is used primarily to flavor salads and to hold a salad together. Many salad dressings are also used as dips. A dip is a flavorful mixture that accompanies foods such as raw vegetables, crackers, or chips. Like salad dressings, dips should complement or enhance a food's flavor.
   REF: 251

2. ANS: The two types of green salad are tossed and composed. Prepare all ingredients individually for either salad. Toss together the ingredients of a tossed green salad prior to plating. Place a tossed salad on a base or serve without further garnish. Composed salads should not be tossed. Arrange the ingredients on the base separately to create the desired taste experience and achieve a high level of visual appeal.
   REF: 225

3. ANS: The purpose of a garnish is to add flavor, color, and texture to dishes. A garnish is meant to draw attention to the food. Garnish should not overwhelm a food or detract from it. Garnishes should be used to create a visual impression and also to add a taste experience.
   REF: 222

Chapter 5
Purchasing and Inventory

True/False

1. ANS: T
REF: 293

2. ANS: T
REF: 315

3. ANS: F
REF: 329

4. ANS: F
REF: 332

5. ANS: F
REF: 336

Multiple Choice

1. ANS: B
REF: 289

2. ANS: D
REF: 290

3. ANS: B
REF: 290

4. ANS: A
REF: 291

5. ANS: D
REF: 291

6. ANS: D
REF: 296

7. ANS: D
REF: 297

8. ANS: D
REF: 298

9. ANS: B
REF: 298

10. ANS: D
REF: 291

11. ANS: B
REF: 318

12. ANS: A
REF: 297

13. ANS: C
REF: 300

14. ANS: C
REF: 300

15. ANS: C
    REF: 310

16. ANS: C
    REF: 312

17. ANS: C
    REF: 314

18. ANS: C
    REF: 314

19. ANS: A
    REF: 314

20. ANS: A
    REF: 314

21. ANS: B
    REF: 315

22. ANS: B
    REF: 315

23. ANS: B
    REF: 315

24. ANS: C
    REF: 316

25. ANS: C
    REF: 318

26. ANS: B
    REF: 318

27. ANS: A
    REF: 318

28. ANS: C
    REF: 318

29. ANS: C
    REF: 326

30. ANS: B
    REF: 328

31. ANS: C
    REF: 331

32. ANS: D
    REF: 331

33. ANS: B
    REF: 332

34. ANS: B
    REF: 333

35. ANS: 334
    REF: 54

36. ANS: B
    REF: 334

37. ANS: A
    REF: 334

38. ANS: D
    REF: 316

39. ANS: B
    REF: 332

40. ANS: B
    REF: 332

Short Answer

1. ANS: Franchisees
   REF: 300

2. ANS: leaders
   REF: 315

3. ANS: reorder point
   REF: 316

4. ANS: Pilfering
   REF: 334

5. ANS: make-or-buy analysis
   REF: 313

Essay

1. ANS: Product specifications, or specs, describe the requirements for a particular product or service that an operation wants to buy. Specifications include the details that help a product or service meet the operation's quality standards. Operations should always document product specifications.

   The parts usually included are acceptable substitutes, acceptable trim, brand new, color, exact name, intended use, market form, packaging, place of origin, pricing, size, temperature, and USDA grade of item.

   REF: 312–313

2. ANS: A make-or-buy analysis compares the price of buying a convenience food with making that item from scratch. Both goods and labor need to be considered when doing a make-or-buy analysis.

   REF: 313

3. ANS: Inventory is a record of all the goods that a restaurant has on hand, both in storage and in the kitchen prep area. Accurate inventory records help the buyer determine how much stock to order at any time, help the manager keep food costs low and profits high, and allow the manager to better plan for future needs.

   REF: 333–334

Chapter 6
Meat, Poultry, and Seafood

True/False

1. ANS: T
   REF: 381

2. ANS: T
   REF: 402

3. ANS: F
   REF: 409

4. ANS: F
   REF: 356

5. ANS: T
   REF: 387

Multiple Choice

1. ANS: B
   REF: 353

2. ANS: D
   REF: 355

3. ANS: A
   REF: 355

4. ANS: B
   REF: 356

5. ANS: A
   REF: 359

6. ANS: D
   REF: 358

7. ANS: D
   REF: 358

8. ANS: A
   REF: 359

9. ANS: C
   REF: 356

10. ANS: C
    REF: 392

11. ANS: B
    REF: 368

12. ANS: D
    REF: 368

13. ANS: C
    REF: 371

14. ANS: B
    REF: 368

15. ANS: D
    REF: 372

16. ANS: A
    REF: 380

17. ANS: B
    REF: 387

18. ANS: B
    REF: 388

19. ANS: C
    REF: 389

20. ANS: A
    REF: 396

21. ANS: A
    REF: 397

22. ANS: B
    REF: 396

23. ANS: D
    REF: 397

24. ANS: C
    REF: 397

25. ANS: D
    REF: 397

26. ANS: A
    REF: 399

27. ANS: D
    REF: 399

28. ANS: C
    REF: 402

29. ANS: C
    REF: 403

30. ANS: D
    REF: 387

31. ANS: D
    REF: 408

32. ANS: C
    REF: 416

33. ANS: C
    REF: 416

34. ANS: D
    REF: 417

35. ANS: A
    REF: 417

36. ANS: C
    REF: 418

37. ANS: B
    REF: 389

38. ANS: D
    REF: 371

39. ANS: A
    REF: 358

40. ANS: C
    REF: 358

Short Answer

1. ANS: yield grade
   REF: 353

2. ANS: Fabrication
   REF: 357

3. ANS: Retail
   REF: 357

4. ANS: mousseline
   REF: 418

5. ANS: Marbling
   REF: 365

Essay

1. ANS: Wrap loosely in air-permeable paper and store under refrigeration at 41°F or below; never tightly wrap meat in plastic wrap; separate different types of meat to prevent cross-contamination; store at proper temperature and under optimal conditions; and always follow sanitary procedures.
   REF: 367

2. ANS: The federal government does not require fish and shellfish inspections. To ensure freshness, the FDA requires that all foodservice operations retain dated shellstock tags for 90 days. Signs of freshness include slick, moist skin; firm, elastic flesh; clear, full eyes; red- or maroon-colored gills; moist, fresh, flexible, full tail and fins; and clean aroma.
   REF: 402

3. ANS: Forcemeat is used in a variety of preparations including quenelle, sausage, and terrine. Mousseline is made of veal, poultry, or fish. Quenelle is mousseline that has been shaped into small, dumpling-shaped ovals and poached in a rich stock or court bouillon.
   REF: 417

Chapter 7
Marketing

True/False

1. ANS: F
REF: 458

2. ANS: T
REF: 486

3. ANS: F
REF: 436

4. ANS: T
REF: 450

5. ANS: T
REF: 436

Multiple Choice

1. ANS: B
REF: 434

2. ANS: C
REF: 434

3. ANS: C
REF: 437

4. ANS: A
REF: 437

5. ANS: B
REF: 437

6. ANS: A
REF: 438

7. ANS: D
REF: 443

8. ANS: C
REF: 448

9. ANS: D
REF: 448

10. ANS: A
REF: 448

11. ANS: C
REF: 450

12. ANS: C
REF: 450

13. ANS: A
REF: 450

14. ANS: B
REF: 450

15. ANS: A
    REF: 450

16. ANS: D
    REF: 451

17. ANS: C
    REF: 451

18. ANS: D
    REF: 451

19. ANS: A
    REF: 452

20. ANS: C
    REF: 453

21. ANS: A
    REF: 457

22. ANS: C
    REF: 457

23. ANS: C
    REF: 457

24. ANS: B
    REF: 438

25. ANS: D
    REF: 460

26. ANS: D
    REF: 461

27. ANS: B
    REF: 463

28. ANS: C
    REF: 471

29. ANS: B
    REF: 472

30. ANS: C
    REF: 472

31. ANS: A
    REF: 458

32. ANS: B
    REF: 472

33. ANS: B
    REF: 473

34. ANS: B
    REF: 473

35. ANS: D
    REF: 473

36. ANS: D
    REF: 483

37. ANS: C
    REF: 484

38. ANS: C
    REF: 487

39. ANS: D
    REF: 489

40. ANS: D
    REF: 489

Short Answer

1. ANS: Publicity
   REF: 461

2. ANS: press release
   REF: 462

3. ANS: Profit
   REF: 483

4. ANS: Marketing
   REF: 434

5. ANS: Demographics
   REF: 45

Essay

1. ANS: Marketing involves the communication and planning for taking a product or service to market. The goal of marketing is to determine the needs and wants of consumers, and to satisfy them. Competition in the restaurant and foodservice industry makes it necessary for managers to use marketing skills to attract customers.
   REF: 434

2. ANS: Market segmentation breaks down the potential market into smaller groups of like individuals. Segment the market in four basic ways:

   - Demographic segmentation—In a community with a lot of young families you might want to open a fun place like Chuck E. Cheese.

   - Geographic segmentation—Knowing people arrive at the plant to work very early and live at least 30 miles away might make a restaurant open even earlier for the breakfast crowd.

   - Product usage segmentation—If the town has a favorite sports team, you might have football nights.

   - Lifestyle segmentation—If you live in a town with a large, young population you might have more quick-service or healthy food operations.

   REF: 450

3. ANS: Market demand is the number of potential customers who have the money and desire to purchase your product or service. Sales histories and forecasting are two common tools used to determine market demand.
   REF: 447

Chapter 8
Desserts and Baked Goods

True/False

1. ANS: F
REF: 516

2. ANS: T
REF: 546

3. ANS: T
REF: 516

4. ANS: F
REF: 528

5. ANS: T
REF: 538

Multiple Choice

1. ANS: D
REF: 504

2. ANS: B
REF: 506

3. ANS: B
REF: 505

4. ANS: D
REF: 505

5. ANS: A
REF: 506

6. ANS: D
REF: 505

7. ANS: C
REF: 506

8. ANS: C
REF: 506

9. ANS: C
REF: 507

10. ANS: C
REF: 514

11. ANS: B
REF: 514

12. ANS: C
REF: 516

13. ANS: A
REF: 525

14. ANS: D
REF: 525

15. ANS: C
REF: 525

16. ANS: B
REF: 527

17. ANS: D
REF: 528

18. ANS: A
REF: 533

19. ANS: D
REF: 535

20. ANS: D
REF: 536

21. ANS: D
REF: 537

22. ANS: B
REF: 539

23. ANS: C
REF: 539

24. ANS: B
REF: 544

25. ANS: D
REF: 546

26. ANS: A
REF: 547

27. ANS: D
REF: 548

28. ANS: C
REF: 548

29. ANS: D
REF: 555

30. ANS: C
REF: 557

31. ANS: B
REF: 556

32. ANS: D
REF: 508

33. ANS: B
REF: 553

34. ANS: B
REF: 537

35. ANS: C
REF: 525

36. ANS: B
REF: 525

37. ANS: C
REF: 544

38. ANS: C
REF: 555

39. ANS: C
REF: 556

40. ANS: B
REF: 539

Short Answer

1. ANS: bloom
   REF: 546

2. ANS: formulas
   REF: 508

3. ANS: Nibs
   REF: 544

4. ANS: torte
   REF: 555

5. ANS: coulis
   REF: 555

Essay

1. ANS: Yeast breads are divided into two categories: lean doughs and rich doughs. Lean doughs are made with flour, yeast, and water. They tend to have a chewy texture and crisp crust. Rich doughs are made with the addition of shortening or tenderizing ingredients, such as sugar, syrup, butter, eggs, milk, and cream. Rich doughs have a cake-like texture after baking.
   REF: 514

2. ANS: Dropped cookies are made from a soft dough and dropped from a spoon or scoop onto the cookie sheet.

   Bagged cookies are made by forcing soft dough through a pastry bag.

   Rolled cookies are cut from a stiff dough that has been rolled out on a baking board.

   Molded cookies are molded by hand into any shape from a stiff dough.

   Icebox cookies are made from dough that has been rolled into logs and chilled, then sliced just before baking.

   Bar cookies are made by baking three or four baking pan-length bars and then slicing them into small bars.
   REF: 539

3. ANS: Sherbets and sorbets are frozen mixtures of fruit juice or fruit purée. Sherbet contains milk and/or eggs for creaminess; sorbet contains no dairy, just fruit juice or purée with sweeteners and other flavors or additives. As a rule, serve sorbet as a first course, as a palate cleanser between courses, or as a dessert. Serve sherbets as a dessert item.
   REF: 553

Chapter 9
Sustainability in the Restaurant and Foodservice Industry

True/False

1. ANS: T
   REF: 579

2. ANS: T
   REF: 582

3. ANS: F
   REF: 609

4. ANS: F
   REF: 621

5. ANS: T
   REF: 626

Multiple Choice

1. ANS: A
   REF: 575

2. ANS: A
   REF: 575

3. ANS: B
   REF: 575

4. ANS: A
   REF: 575

5. ANS: D
   REF: 575

6. ANS: C
   REF: 577

7. ANS: B
   REF: 577

8. ANS: B
   REF: 586

9. ANS: C
   REF: 588

10. ANS: D
    REF: 588

11. ANS: B
    REF: 588

12. ANS: D
    REF: 589

13. ANS: A
    REF: 595

14. ANS: C
    REF: 602

15. ANS: C
    REF: 602

16. ANS: A
    REF: 603

17. ANS: B
    REF: 604

18. ANS: C
    REF: 605

19. ANS: D
    REF: 580

20. ANS: C
    REF: 580

21. ANS: C
    REF: 609

22. ANS: A
    REF: 614

23. ANS: B
    REF: 617

24. ANS: A
    REF: 619

25. ANS: C
    REF: 619

26. ANS: D
    REF: 620

27. ANS: A
    REF: 621

28. ANS: B
    REF: 623

29. ANS: C
    REF: 624

30. ANS: B
    REF: 626

31. ANS: C
    REF: 579

32. ANS: A
    REF: 578

33. ANS: A
    REF: 578

34. ANS: B
    REF: 588

35. ANS: D
    REF: 617

36. ANS: C
    REF: 623

37. ANS: D
    REF: 579

38. ANS: A
    REF: 580

39. ANS: C
    REF: 594

40. ANS: C
    REF: 618

Short Answer

1. ANS: Sustainability
   REF: 575

2. ANS: green
   REF: 594

3. ANS: recycling
   REF: 605

4. ANS: Aquaculture
   REF: 619

5. ANS: Open
   REF: 621

Essay

1. ANS: Water conservation is important because droughts reduce water levels and many parts of the world are already experiencing water shortages. Without water, crops and animals will die, which limits the food supply and raises prices; businesses and farms close; brushfires and dust storms increase; and residents may move out of areas, thus overpopulating other areas.
   REF: 575

2. ANS: Restaurant and foodservice operations can reduce by limiting the garbage they make. They can do this by accurate production forecasting, purchasing only what they have storage space for, and asking suppliers to reduce their packaging and shipping.
   REF: 604

3. ANS: Turn off the lights when not in use, make sure dishwasher loads are full, power down idle equipment, seal off unused areas, reduce idle times, clean and maintain equipment regularly, and replace incandescent lighting.
   REF: 590

Chapter 10
Global Cuisine 1: The Americas

True/False

1. ANS: T
    REF: 650

2. ANS: T
    REF: 656

3. ANS: F
    REF: 668

4. ANS: F
    REF: 678

5. ANS: T
    REF: 656

Multiple Choice

1. ANS: A
    REF: 639

2. ANS: D
    REF: 639

3. ANS: D
    REF: 640

4. ANS: B
    REF: 642

5. ANS: B
    REF: 643

6. ANS: A
    REF: 643

7. ANS: B
    REF: 645

8. ANS: B
    REF: 646

9. ANS: A
    REF: 646

10. ANS: A
    REF: 647

11. ANS: C
    REF: 647

12. ANS: D
    REF: 648

13. ANS: C
    REF: 650

14. ANS: B
    REF: 652

15. ANS: B
    REF: 664

16. ANS: A
    REF: 664

17. ANS: A
    REF: 668

18. ANS: C
    REF: 670

19. ANS: A
    REF: 674

20. ANS: C
    REF: 678

21. ANS: A
    REF: 681

22. ANS: D
    REF: 646

23. ANS: C
    REF: 649

24. ANS: A
    REF: 638

25. ANS: B
    REF: 647

26. ANS: C
    REF: 647

27. ANS: C
    REF: 652

28. ANS: A
    REF: 662

29. ANS: D
    REF: 664

30. ANS: C
    REF: 666

31. ANS: C
    REF: 668

32. ANS: D
    REF: 678

33. ANS: D
    REF: 666

34. ANS: B
    REF: 668

35. ANS: C
    REF: 657

36. ANS: D
    REF: 652

37. ANS: D
    REF: 656

38. ANS: C
    REF: 676

39. ANS: C
    REF: 643

40. ANS: D
    REF: 650

Short Answer

1. ANS: Creole
    REF: 646

2. ANS: Trinity
    REF: 647

3. ANS: fusion
    REF: 652

4. ANS: *Curtido*
    REF: 664

5. ANS: Mole
    REF: 657

Essay

1. ANS: Sometimes referred to as Asian fusion or Euro-Pacific, Pacific Rim cuisine was created in the early 1970s when many eclectic styles of fusion cuisine became popular. Pacific Rim cuisine is influenced by many different countries bordering the Pacific Ocean. It is a style of cooking and presenting foods that combines the ingredients and techniques of Asian and West Coast cuisines. Pacific Rim flavors are based on seafood, sourdough bread, and local fruits and vegetables.
    REF: 652–654

2. ANS: Southwestern United States flavors compared to Pacific Coast flavors:

    Pacific Coast flavors are based on seafood, sourdough bread, and local fruits and vegetables, while Southwestern flavors are based on edible plants found in a desert region, such as pine nuts, cactus and peppers.

    Pacific Coast cuisine is influenced by Asian fusion due to the impact of Thai and Chinese immigrants to the area, while Southwestern cuisine is influenced by the Mexican and American Indian cultures.

    While beef and pork are popular in the Southwest along with rabbit, deer, and wild turkey, in the Pacific Coast region seafood is used in abundance. Examples of these are salmon, halibut, mussels and oysters. Other staples of the diet include poultry, coconut, bananas, pineapple, and tropical fruits.

    The differences in the two regions' cuisines are due in part to the influences of other cultures, but also to the climate. The Pacific region benefits from rainfall and fertile soil while the Southwest is arid and dry.
    REF: 644, 652

3. ANS: Mexican cuisine, as well as related regional cuisines, is common in the United States because of the long border we share with Mexico. The flavor profile of Mexico is spicy, hot, and earthy, and these flavors have joined the mainstream of the United States. Examples of Mexican dishes include enchiladas, tacos, and tamales. Although they are cooked and served differently in the United States, they are common to our cuisine. Tex-Mex is an offshoot of Mexican cuisine originating in Texas, while Cal-Mex originated in California as a direct influence of Mexican cuisine.

REF: 655–657

Chapter 11
Global Cuisine 2: Europe, the Mediterranean, the Middle East, and Asia

True/False

1. ANS: F
   REF: 697

2. ANS: T
   REF: 700

3. ANS: T
   REF: 712

4. ANS: T
   REF: 726

5. ANS: F
   REF: 742

Multiple Choice

1. ANS: B
   REF: 697

2. ANS: A
   REF: 698

3. ANS: D
   REF: 698

4. ANS: B
   REF: 698

5. ANS: C
   REF: 699

6. ANS: A
   REF: 699

7. ANS: A
   REF: 701

8. ANS: B
   REF: 701

9. ANS: A
   REF: 701

10. ANS: A
    REF: 704

11. ANS: B
    REF: 705

12. ANS: A
    REF: 711

13. ANS: C
    REF: 712

14. ANS: D
    REF: 712

15. ANS: A
    REF: 714

16. ANS: B
    REF: 716

17. ANS: B
    REF: 717

18. ANS: C
    REF: 717

19. ANS: C
    REF: 720

20. ANS: C
    REF: 727

21. ANS: B
    REF: 727

22. ANS: A
    REF: 730

23. ANS: D
    REF: 730

24. ANS: D
    REF: 732

25. ANS: B
    REF: 738

26. ANS: A
    REF: 738

27. ANS: D
    REF: 741

28. ANS: A
    REF: 741

29. ANS: C
    REF: 742

30. ANS: B
    REF: 743

31. ANS: A
    REF: 744

32. ANS: C
    REF: 747

33. ANS: B
    REF: 748

34. ANS: B
    REF: 750

35. ANS: B
    REF: 712

36. ANS: D
    REF: 713

37. ANS: B
    REF: 717

38. ANS: A
    REF: 714

39. ANS: A
    REF: 702

40. ANS: D
    REF: 701

Short Answer

1. ANS: Mandarin
   REF: 742

2. ANS: soy sauce
   REF: 742

3. ANS: tempura
   REF: 744

4. ANS: *dum*
   REF: 749

5. ANS: Kebob *meshwi*
   REF: 733

Essay

1. ANS: In India, Hinduism promotes vegetarianism. In China, the cuisine is based on the yin and yang philosophy of the Tao, the belief that a single guiding principle orders the universe. Foods should not be forced to become something they are not and should be kept in their most natural and pure states. Buddhism, in particular, has been a fundamental influence on Chinese lifestyles and cuisine. This religion emphasizes balance, serenity, and peace, which has led to the rise of vegetarianism and the simultaneous development of a number of innovative meat substitutes, especially those based on bean curd.
   REF: 738, 747

2. ANS: The weather influences what can be grown, while the terrain of the land influences where plants and animals can be raised. The availability of water greatly influences what type of plant will grow, such as rice, which needs much water. The philosophy of the local people (such as Tao, which is the belief that a single, guiding principle orders the universe and foods should not be forced to become something they are not) also has an impact.

   The religious beliefs of a people often influence what they will eat, such as Buddhism, where one does not eat meat. The conquering of lands by people from other regions and cultures, and the foods and spices they introduced to the conquered area also had an impact on cuisine. Other influences include transportation availability, neighboring regions, and exploration and trade.
   REF: Various

3. ANS: Greek salad—mainly tomatoes with romaine lettuce, garlic, feta cheese, Parmesan cheese. Similar to our tossed salad, just more tomatoes.

Hummus—puréed chickpeas seasoned with lemon juice, olive oil, and sesame seed paste. Similar to our ranch dip.

Moussaka—a layered dish of lamb, eggplant, béchamel sauce. Similar to meatloaf.

Baklava—a honey-sweetened pastry made of phyllo dough and chopped nuts, similar to Danish without the fruit.

REF: 716–718

Final 1

True/False

1. ANS: T
   REF: 17
   CH: 1

2. ANS: F
   REF: 57
   CH: 1

3. ANS: T
   REF: 100
   CH: 2

4. ANS: T
   REF: 117
   CH: 2

5. ANS: T
   REF: 170
   CH: 3

6. ANS: T
   REF: 151
   CH: 3

7. ANS: F
   REF: 248
   CH: 4

8. ANS: F
   REF: 235
   CH: 4

9. ANS: T
   REF: 314
   CH: 5

10. ANS: F
    REF: 329
    CH: 5

11. ANS: T
    REF: 355
    CH: 6

12. ANS: T
    REF: 365
    CH: 6

13. ANS: T
    REF: 462
    CH: 7

14. ANS: T
    REF: 486
    CH: 7

15. ANS: F
    REF: 528
    CH: 8

16. ANS: T
    REF: 553
    CH: 8

17. ANS: F
    REF: 609
    CH: 9

18. ANS: T
    REF: 601
    CH: 9

19. ANS: T
    REF: 664
    CH: 10

20. ANS: F
    REF: 670
    CH: 10

21. ANS: F
    REF: 697
    CH: 11

22. ANS: T
    REF: 712
    CH: 11

Multiple Choice

1. ANS: A
   REF: 17
   CH: 1

2. ANS: C
   REF: 25
   CH: 1

3. ANS: C
   REF: 57
   CH: 1

4. ANS: D
   REF: 55
   CH: 1

5. ANS: A
   REF: 28
   CH: 1

6. ANS: A
   REF: 25
   CH: 1

7. ANS: D
   REF: 58
   CH: 1

8. ANS: D
   REF: 84
   CH: 2

9. ANS: C
   REF: 90
   CH: 2

10. ANS: A
    REF: 94
    CH: 2

11. ANS: B
    REF: 101
    CH: 2

12. ANS: D
    REF: 87
    CH: 2

13. ANS: D
    REF: 95
    CH: 2

14. ANS: B
    REF: 100
    CH: 2

15. ANS: C
    REF: 106
    CH: 2

16. ANS: D
    REF: 153
    CH: 3

17. ANS: D
    REF: 156
    CH: 3

18. ANS: A
    REF: 205
    CH: 3

19. ANS: A
    REF: 201
    CH: 3

20. ANS: B
    REF: 178
    CH: 3

21. ANS: D
    REF: 220
    CH: 4

22. ANS: C
    REF: 222
    CH: 4

23. ANS: D
    REF: 235
    CH: 4

24. ANS: A
    REF: 238
    CH: 4

25. ANS: C
    REF: 246
    CH: 4

26. ANS: C
    REF: 252
    CH: 4

27. ANS: D
    REF: 225
    CH: 4

28. ANS: A
    REF: 291
    CH: 5

29. ANS: C
    REF: 326
    CH: 5

30. ANS: A
    REF: 316
    CH: 5

31. ANS: D
    REF: 300
    CH: 5

32. ANS: D
    REF: 314
    CH: 5

33. ANS: A
    REF: 315
    CH: 5

34. ANS: C
    REF: 353
    CH: 6

35. ANS: C
    REF: 417
    CH: 6

36. ANS: C
    REF: 387
    CH: 6

37. ANS: C
    REF: 403
    CH: 6

38. ANS: A
    REF: 402
    CH: 6

39. ANS: C
    REF: 358
    CH: 6

40. ANS: D
    REF: 355
    CH: 6

41. ANS: B
    REF: 437
    CH: 7

42. ANS: B
    REF: 438

43. ANS: D
    REF: 448
    CH: 7

44. ANS: B
    REF: 450
    CH: 7

45. ANS: D
    REF: 471
    CH: 7

46. ANS: D
    REF: 489
    CH: 7

47. ANS: D
    REF: 473
    CH: 7

48. ANS: B
    REF: 506
    CH: 8

49. ANS: B
    REF: 514
    CH: 8

50. ANS: A
    REF: 525
    CH: 8

51. ANS: B
    REF: 504
    CH: 8

52. ANS: B
    REF: 514
    CH: 8

53. ANS: C
    REF: 546
    CH: 8

54. ANS: D
    REF: 555
    CH: 8

55. ANS: B
    REF: 588
    CH: 9

56. ANS: C
    REF: 575
    CH: 9

57. ANS: B
    REF: 575
    CH: 9

58. ANS: D
    REF: 589
    CH: 9

59. ANS: A
    REF: 608
    CH: 9

60. ANS: B
    REF:623

CH: 9

61. ANS: D
REF: 652
CH: 10

62. ANS: C
REF: 668
CH: 10

63. ANS: B
REF: 662
CH: 10

64. ANS: C
REF: 648
CH: 10

65. ANS: D
REF: 647
CH: 10

66. ANS: B
REF: 646
CH: 10

67. ANS: A

REF: 643
CH: 10

68. ANS: C
REF: 699
CH: 11

69. ANS: A
REF: 704
CH: 11

70. ANS: C
REF: 711
CH: 11

71. ANS: D
REF: 730
CH: 11

72. ANS: C
REF: 738
CH: 11

73. ANS: A
REF: 738
CH: 11

Short Answer:

1. ANS: pasteurized
REF: 6
CH: 1

2. ANS: yolk
REF: 17
CH: 1

3. ANS: Shocking
REF: 24
CH: 1

4. ANS: calories
REF: 85
CH: 2

5. ANS: pesticides
REF: 126
CH: 2

6. ANS: Iron
REF: 95
CH: 2

7. ANS: average check
   REF: 178
   CH: 3

8. ANS: crew schedule
   REF: 191
   CH: 3

9. ANS: Cost
   REF: 147
   CH: 3

10. ANS: Dessert
    REF: 235
    CH: 4

11. ANS: Vinaigrette
    REF: 244
    CH: 4

12. ANS: Mayonnaise
    REF: 248
    CH: 4

13. ANS: Bids
    REF: 300
    CH: 5

14. ANS: production
    REF: 314
    CH: 5

15. ANS: Par stock
    REF: 315
    CH: 5

16. ANS: Yield grade
    REF: 353
    CH: 6

17. ANS: Forcemeat
    REF: 417
    CH: 6

18. ANS: Offal
    REF: 359
    CH: 6

19. ANS: Community relations
    REF: 461
    CH: 7

20. ANS: sales mix analysis
    REF: 486
    CH: 7

21. ANS: California
    REF: 492
    CH: 7

22. ANS: caramelization
    REF: 505
    CH: 8

23. ANS: extracts
    REF: 507
    CH: 8

24. ANS: flour
    REF: 508
    CH: 8

25. ANS: green
    REF: 594
    CH: 9

26. ANS: Repurposed food
    REF: 602
    CH: 9

27. ANS: local
    REF: 614
    CH: 9

28. ANS: Gumbo
    REF: 647
    CH: 10

29. ANS: Caribbean

REF: 668

CH: 10

30. ANS: Cacao

REF: 664

CH: 10

31. ANS: *tagine*

REF: 713

CH: 11

32. ANS: Szechwan Hunan

REF: 741

CH: 11

33. ANS: *Polow*

REF: 730

CH: 11

Essay

1. ANS: The USDA assigns two grades for most types of meat—quality grade and yield grade. Some types of meat may be one of these grades, and other types may have both.

    Quality grade measures the flavor characteristics of meat products. The USDA evaluates meat for traits that indicate its tenderness, juiciness, and flavor. Quality grades for beef, lamb, and veal can include prime, choice, select, standard, commercial, utility, cutter, cull, or canner. Unlike other types of meat, pork does not receive a quality grade. Although the USDA inspects pork for wholesomeness, pork is graded only for yield and receives a yield grade stamp.

    Yield grade measures the proportion of edible or usable meat after being trimmed of bones or fat. You can get yield grades for beef, pork, and lamb products. This is helpful because the differences in the amount of fat on the outside of the meat can cause the yield of usable product to vary.

    REF: 353

    CH: 6

2. ANS: Yeast breads are divided into two categories—lean doughs and rich doughs.

    Lean doughs are made with flour, yeast, water, and salt. They have very little or no sugar or fat. Breads made from lean dough tend to have a chewy texture and a crisp crust. French bread and hard rolls are examples of lean doughs.

    Rich doughs are made with the addition of shortening or tenderizing ingredients such as sugars, syrups, butter, eggs, milk, and cream. Introducing these ingredients changes the bread's overall texture, as well as the way the dough is handled. Rich doughs should have a cake-like texture after baking. Parker House rolls, cloverleaf rolls, soft rolls, and Danish are examples of rich doughs.

    REF: 514

    CH: 8

3. ANS: Traditionally, Italian food has been characterized as *la cucina povera* (the cuisine of poverty)—simple, filling, and delicious dishes made by using all ingredients as carefully as possible. Olive oil, semolina, and the extravagant use of vegetables define this cuisine. Italian cooking methods include braising, boiling, roasting (either on a spit or in a wood-burning oven), grilling, and deep-frying.

The complex Moroccan cuisine is sweet, sour, and spicy. Rich, full-flavored stews, steamed dishes, and roasts predominate. Moroccan cooking methods focus on *tagine, couscoussière,* steaming, and spit-roasting.

REF: 712–713

CH: 11

4. ANS:

- Purchasing: An operation must be spending wisely and getting good quality product for cost. Establishing quality standards is essential in acquiring and producing consistent, top-quality product.

- Receiving: An operation must be sure that it is getting what it's paying for, both in quality and quantity, from its vendors. Management or well-trained staff need to be in charge of receiving to ensure quality standards and accuracy of orders.

- Storage: Proper storage of goods is essential. Storage facilities must be safe, sanitary, and efficient. Operations must continually monitor freezers and refrigerated storage units to make sure they are running as they should be. Improperly stored food will be wasted, and wasted food increases food costs.

- Issuing: An efficient issuing system, also known as inventory control, allows operations to control food costs in a number of ways. It keeps a record of what product is being used most frequently (that is, what's selling), and it also helps prevent pilfering.

- Preparation: Efficient food preparation is crucial to controlling food costs. All product should be used to the fullest, so operations should have detailed specifications as to exactly how every food item should be prepared for cooking.

- Cooking (production): The way in which food is prepared and portioned is obviously an important stage in the food flow process. Incorrectly cooked food goes to waste, and incorrectly portioned food also results in waste, both of which add to food costs.

- Service (sale): Service is the final stage in the process, but no less important than the previous stages. Good service is crucial to moving product that needs to be moved, as well as correctly taking orders so that mistakes aren't made in the kitchen. Any mistakes made at the service level can both directly and indirectly contribute to increased food costs.

REF: 165–166

CH: 3

5. ANS: The two types of vitamins are water-soluble and fat-soluble. Water-soluble vitamins mix only with water, and fat-soluble vitamins mix only with fat.

- Water-soluble vitamins (vitamins C and B) are found in food such as oranges and grapefruit. The body needs these vitamin sources every day. These vitamins are vulnerable to cooking and may be destroyed by heat or washed away by steam or water.

- Fat-soluble vitamins (vitamins A, D, E, and K) are found in food containing fat. They are stored in the liver and body fat. The body draws on these stored vitamins when needed.

REF: 94

CH: 2

Final 2

True/False

1. ANS: F
   REF: 25
   CH: 1

2. ANS: T
   REF: 16
   CH: 1

3. ANS: T
   REF: 100
   CH: 2

4. ANS: T
   REF: 88
   CH: 2

5. ANS: T
   REF: 168
   CH: 3

6. ANS: F
   REF: 148
   CH: 3

7. ANS: T
   REF: 244
   CH: 4

8. ANS: F
   REF: 244
   CH: 4

9. ANS: T
   REF: 334
   CH: 5

10. ANS: T
    REF: 326
    CH: 5

11. ANS: F
    REF: 360
    CH: 6

12. ANS: T
    REF: 381
    CH: 6

13. ANS: T
    REF: 450
    CH: 7

14. ANS: F
    REF: 483
    CH: 7

15. ANS: T
    REF: 524
    CH: 8

16. ANS: T
    REF: 533
    CH: 8

17. ANS: F
    REF: 575
    CH: 9

18. ANS: T
    REF: 595
    CH: 9

19. ANS: F
    REF: 656
    CH: 10

20. ANS: T
    REF: 656
    CH: 10

21. ANS: T
    REF: 732
    CH: 11

22. ANS: T
    REF: 738
    CH: 11

Multiple Choice

1. ANS: A
   REF: 19
   CH: 1

2. ANS: B
   REF: 17
   CH: 1

3. ANS: C
   REF: 16
   CH: 1

4. ANS: A
   REF: 14
   CH: 1

5. ANS: D
   REF: 25
   CH: 1

6. ANS: D
   REF: 25
   CH: 1

7. ANS: A
   REF: 54
   CH: 1

8. ANS: D
   REF: 90
   CH: 2

9. ANS: C
   REF: 91
   CH: 2

10. ANS: D
    REF: 92
    CH: 2

11. ANS: A
    REF: 93
    CH: 2

12. ANS: C
    REF: 27
    CH: 2

13. ANS: D
    REF: 113
    CH: 2

14. ANS: A
    REF: 88
    CH: 2

15. ANS: C
    REF: 100
    CH: 2

16. ANS: A
    REF: 153
    CH: 3

17. ANS: A
    REF: 147
    CH: 3

18. ANS: B
    REF: 167
    CH: 3

19. ANS: D
    REF: 148
    CH: 3

20. ANS: A
    REF: 202
    CH: 3

21. ANS: C
    REF: 220
    CH: 4

22. ANS: A
    REF: 221
    CH: 4

23. ANS: A
    REF: 235
    CH: 4

24. ANS: B
    REF: 237
    CH: 4

25. ANS: D
    REF: 244
    CH: 4

26. ANS: B
    REF: 235
    CH: 4

27. ANS: C
    REF: 258
    CH: 4

28. ANS: C
    REF: 316
    CH: 5

29. ANS: D
    REF: 291
    CH: 5

30. ANS: D
    REF: 300
    CH: 5

31. ANS: D
    REF: 310
    CH: 5

32. ANS: C
    REF: 318
    CH: 5

33. ANS: D
    REF: 326
    CH: 5

34. ANS: B
    REF: 358
    CH: 6

35. ANS: D
    REF: 399
    CH: 6

36. ANS: D
    REF: 397
    CH: 6

37. ANS: A
    REF: 396
    CH: 6

38. ANS: C
    REF: 371
    CH: 6

39. ANS: D
    REF: 358
    CH: 6

40. ANS: A
    REF: 396
    CH: 6

41. ANS: C
    REF: 434
    CHL 7

42. ANS: A
    REF: 434
    CH: 7

43. ANS: C
    REF: 437
    CH: 7

44. ANS: B
    REF: 448
    CH: 7

45. ANS: B
    REF: 450
    CH: 7

46. ANS: C
    REF: 451
    CH: 7

47. ANS: A
    REF: 472
    CH: 7

48. ANS: D
    REF: 507
    CH: 8

49. ANS: D
    REF: 539
    CH: 8

50. ANS: A
    REF: 525
    CH: 8

51. ANS: A
    REF: 516
    CH: 8

52. ANS: A
    REF: 533
    CH: 8

53. ANS: A
    REF: 555
    CH: 8

54. ANS: D
    REF: 548
    CH: 8

55. ANS: C
    REF: 588
    CH: 9

56. ANS: B
    REF: 575

57. ANS: B
    REF: 577
    CH: 9

58. ANS: C
    REF: 602
    CH: 9

59. ANS: B
    REF: 579
    CH: 9

60. ANS: C
    REF: 575
    CH: 9

61. ANS: C
    REF: 650
    CH: 10

62. ANS: D
    REF: 649
    CH: 10

63. ANS: B
    REF: 652
    CH: 10

64. ANS: A
    REF: 646
    CH: 10

65. ANS: D
    REF: 664
    CH: 10

66. ANS: A
    REF: 681
    CH: 10

67. ANS: A
    REF: 674
    CH: 10

68. ANS: A
    REF: 699
    CH: 11

69. ANS: A
    REF: 712
    CH: 11

70. ANS: D
    REF: 717
    CH: 11

71. ANS: C
    REF: 740
    CH: 11

72. ANS: A
    REF: 702
    CH: 11

73. ANS: A
    REF: 741
    CH: 11

Short Answer:

1. ANS: Pooled
   REF: 27
   CH: 1

2. ANS: Pizza
   REF: 54
   CH: 1

3. ANS: Tea
   REF: 56
   CH: 1

4. ANS: phytochemicals
   REF: 84
   CH: 2

5. ANS: organic
   REF: 127
   CH: 2

6. ANS: Dietary Reference Intakes
   REF: 99
   CH: 2

7. ANS: Contribution margin
REF: 178
CH: 3

8. ANS: forecast
REF: 152
CH: 3

9. ANS: Inventory
REF: 167
CH: 3

10. ANS: intermezzo
REF: 235
CH: 4

11. ANS: stockout
REF: 314
CH: 4

12. ANS: purchase order
REF: 316
CH: 4

13. ANS: credit memo
REF: 328
CH: 5

14. ANS: cash position
REF: 289
CH: 5

15. ANS: Humidity
REF: 332
CH: 5

16. ANS: aging
REF: 356
CH: 6

17. ANS: Finfish
REF: 397
CH: 6

18. ANS: Shucking
REF: 401
CH: 6

19. ANS: marketing
REF: 434
CH: 7

20. ANS: Mass
REF: 450
CH: 7

21. ANS: Demographics
REF: 450
CH: 7

22. ANS: Baking blind
REF: 535
CH: 8

23. ANS: tempering
REF: 547
CH: 8

24. ANS: curdle
REF: 555
CH: 8

25. ANS: fossil fuels
REF: 586
CH: 9

26. ANS: Renewable energy sources
REF: 587
CH: 9

27. ANS: Composting
REF: 609
CH: 9

28. ANS: shredded
REF: 650
CH: 10

29. ANS: Mole

REF: 657

CH: 10

30. ANS: *pupusa*

REF: 666

CH: 10

31. ANS: *dum*

REF: 749

CH: 11

32. ANS: Tao

REF: 738

CH: 11

33. ANS: semolina

REF: 702

CH: 11

Essay

1. ANS: The fat content of buttermilk depends on the type of milk used, while the fat content of evaporated milk is at last 6.5 percent and the fat content of condensed milk is at least 8.5 percent.

   Buttermilk is made of fresh liquid milk that has bacteria added to it to make it sour. Evaporated milk is made by removing 60 percent of the water. Condensed milk is made by removing 60 percent of the water from whole milk and adding sugar.

   REF: 8

   CH: 1

2. ANS: Base: The base of a salad is usually a layer of salad greens that line the plate or bowl in which the salad will be served. Use smaller leafy greens, cup-shaped Boston lettuce, or iceberg lettuce leaves to give height to salads and form edible containers. Also use romaine, Belgian endive, and leaf lettuce as a salad base.

   Body: The body of the salad consists of the main ingredients. The body can be a mixture of vegetables, such as lettuce, tomatoes, carrots, etc.; meats, such as turkey breast or ham; or cheeses and various fruits, such as mandarin oranges or apples. Use mayonnaise-based salads, such as tuna salad or crabmeat salad, as a salad body placed on a base of lettuce.

   Garnish: Garnish enhances the salad's appearance while also complementing its overall taste. A garnish should be something that will be eaten with the body, functioning as a flavor component. Simple garnishes are the best. For example, mix shredded carrot or a fine julienne of red bell pepper with salad greens, or lightly toss them with seasoning and then place them on top of the greens.

Dressing: Salad dressings are liquids or semiliquids used to flavor salads. They act as a sauce that holds the salad together. Dressings can range from mayonnaise for potato- or macaroni-based salads to vinaigrettes for lettuce-based salads. Sometimes dressings are called cold sauces because their purpose is to flavor, moisten, and enrich foods. Use tart or sour dressings for green salads and vegetable salads. Use slightly sweetened dressings for fruit salads. Mix some dressings with the ingredients ahead of time, such as for "bound salad." Add some dressings at plating and service to bring an additional flavor aspect to the final product.

REF: 4

CH: 221–222

3. ANS: The contemporary marketing mix has 3 key elements—the product-service mix, the presentation mix, and the communication mix.

The product-service mix consists of all of the food and services offered to customers. The presentation mix consists of all the elements that make the operation look unique, such as layout, color scheme, furniture, uniforms, etc. The communication mix includes all of the ways an operation actively tries to reach, or communicate, with its desired customers, such as television, radio, newspapers, flyers, or Web sites, or its menu, customer survey requests, and other customer feedback requests.

REF: 436–437

CH: 7

4. ANS: There are many ways in which to conserve water, including:

- Thaw food in the cooler.

- Soak and scrape first: Dirty cookware and dishes should be precleaned by scraping or soaking off as much food as possible in standing water (rather than a running flow).

- Keep water temperature at the right level.

- Load dishwashers correctly: Make sure racks are full (but not stuffed) before sending them through.

- Repair leaks quickly.

- Don't automatically serve water: Customers who would like to have water will request it.

- Sweep the outside areas: Don't use water hoses to clean sidewalks and parking lots.

- Train employees to conserve.

REF: 578–579

CH: 9

5. ANS: Traditional New England recipes are not highly seasoned. The flavors are deep and rich, and tend to be more mild than spicy.

Midwestern cuisine is generally hearty, but light-handed with seasonings, preferring sage, dill, caraway, mustard, and parsley to bold and spicy flavors.

The flavor profiles of the Southern regions vary from the highly flavored, spicy Cajun dishes to the more mild but full-flavored cuisine of the tidewater region. In all cases, they are fresh flavors that speak of the local ingredients.

The Southwest favors smoky and spicy flavors.

Asian fusion flavors range from sweet and sour to bland due to the influences of Thai and Chinese cuisines. The Thai and Chinese believe that food should be served in its natural state. Additional Pacific Coast flavors are based in seafood, sourdough bread, and local fruits and vegetables.

REF: 638, 642, 644, 649, 653

CH: 10